THE COMPLETE CHAINSAW AND CROSSCUT SAW BOOK

THE AUTHORITY ON SAW EQUIPMENT, TECHNIQUE, USE, MAINTENANCE, AND TIMBER WORK

BY THE **U.S. FOREST SERVICE**

LEGACY EDITION

THE LIBRARY OF AMERICAN OUTDOORS CLASSICS
BOOK 14

FEATURING

REMASTERED CLASSIC WORKS OF THE HIGHEST QUALITY

FROM **THE TIMELESS MASTERS AND TEACHERS** OF CAMPING,

OUTDOORS SKILLS, WOODCRAFT, AND TRADITIONAL HANDCRAFTS

Doublebit Press
Eugene, OR

INTRODUCTION

To The Doublebit Press Legacy Edition

This deluxe Legacy Edition of *The Complete Chainsaw and Crosscut Saw Book* is a high-quality reissue of three authoritative US Forest Service manuals on saw use. This compilation includes *The Chain Saw and Crosscut Saw Use Training Course*, *The Crosscut Saw Manual,* and *Saws That Sing,* unabridged from their original sources. This volume is a must-have on the bookshelf of any outdoors enthusiast, woodsman, lumberjack, camping fan, homesteader, rancher, bushcrafter, or anyone learning how to master the chainsaw or crosscut "misery whip" saw.

The three books in this volume are THE authority in chainsaw and crosscut saw use. Each have numerous descriptive illustrations that give readers exactly what they need to learn about their saw and become an expert in saw lore. Technique and history are covered for both modern chainsaws and manual one-person and two-person crosscut saws. Perfect for folks who clear trails in the wilderness, or want to buck up logs in an efficient way.

This book contains key information on both chainsaws and crosscut saws, including basic cutting principles, blade and cutter care, sharpening, maintenance, storage, safe carrying and transportation, proper safe technique for various situations, tree physics, clothing and equipment for cutters, sawyer history, tree felling and proper notching, and plenty of additional reading references.

Become a timber master with this essential textbook that collects the finest materials on saw use that the Forest Service has published!

About the Library of American Outdoors Classics

The old experts of the woods and mountains taught timeless principles and skills for decades. Through their books, the old experts offered rich descriptions of the outdoor world and encouraged learning through personal experiences in nature. Over the last 125 years, camping, outdoors recreation, and woods activities have substantially changed. Many things have gotten simpler as gear has improved, and life outside or on the trail now brings with it many of the same comforts enjoyed in town. In addition, some activities of the olden days are now no longer in vogue, or are even outright considered inappropriate or illegal, such as high-impact camping practices like chopping down live trees. However, despite many of the positive changes in outdoors methods that have occurred over the years, *there are many other skills and much knowledge that have been forgotten* from the golden era of American outdoors recreation.

By publishing the Library of American Outdoors Classics, it is our goal at Doublebit Press to do what we can to preserve and share the works from forgotten teachers that form the cornerstone of the history of the American outdoors. Through remastered reprint editions of timeless classics of outdoor recreation, perhaps we can regain some of this lost knowledge for future generations.

Because there were fewer options for finding outdoors gear in the early 1900's, experts in *"woodcraft"* skills (not to be confused with today's use of the word to mean woodworking or making things of wood) had to have a deep knowledge of the basic building blocks of outdoor living. This involved not only surviving in the outdoors, but to also have a comfortable and enjoyable time. As Nessmuk puts it in his book *Woodcraft,* "We do not go to the woods to rough it; we go to smooth it — we get it rough enough in town. But let us live the simple, natural life in the woods, and leave all frills behind." Nessmuk did not advocate for folks to go outside and have a terrible time. That would be contrary to the whole point of getting outside. Instead, he advocated for a "simpler" life by leaving some of the creature comforts of the city behind, but also entering the outdoors in a smart and practiced way that made the experience a much more satisfying vacation from home. The goal is to be comfortable so you can focus on having a good time outside and take in everything exposure to nature can offer. However, to be comfortable, one has to know the ins and outs of camping and outdoors life. Despite all the advances in campcraft and outdoors recreation, the old masters of the woods would all likely argue that this will only come from practicing the basics.

Because there was no market yet for specialty outdoors recreational gear (and thus, few outfitters), most outdoors gear came from military surplus piles or was custom made. As such, the old masters of woodcraft often made their own gear suited to their tastes. Through much experience in the woods and field, the great outdoors experts had to know why things worked the way they did by understanding the great web of cause and effect in nature. They had to learn from experience why certain gear worked better in different conditions or know how to solve problems off-the-cuff when things got hairy. They used the basic blocks of camping and outdoors knowledge to fine-tune their gear. They gained experience whenever they could and tried things different ways so they could gain mastery over the fundamentals and see challenges from many angles.

Today, much of the outdoor experience has been greatly simplified by neatly arranged campsites at public campgrounds and gear that has been meticulously improved and tested in both the lab and the field. Many modern conveniences are only a brief trek away, with many parks, campgrounds, and even forests having easy-access roads, convenience stores, and even cell phone signal. In some ways, it is much easier to camp and go outdoors today, and that is a good thing! We should not be miserable when we go outside — lovers of the outdoors know the essential restorative capability that the woods can have on the body, mind, and soul. Although things have gotten easier on us in the 21st Century when it comes to the outdoors, it certainly does not mean that we should forget the foundations of outdoors lore, though. All modern camping skills, outdoors equipment, and cool gizmos that make our lives easier are all founded on principles of the outdoors that the old masters knew well and taught to those who would listen.

Every woods master had their own curriculum or thought some things were more important than others. This includes the present author — certain things appear in this book that other masters leave out of theirs. The old masters also taught common things in slightly different ways or did things differently than others. That's what makes each of the experts different and worth reading. There's no universal way of doing something, especially now. Learning to go about something differently helps with mastery or learn a new skill altogether. Again, to use the metaphor from the above paragraphs, outdoors skills mastery consists of learning the basic building blocks of outdoors living, woods and nature lore, and the art of packing properly for trips. Each master goes about describing these building blocks differently or shows a different aspect of them.

Therefore, we have decided to publish this *Legacy Edition* in our Library of American Outdoors Classics series. This book is an important contribution to the early American recreational outdoors literature and has important historical and collector value toward preserving the American outdoors tradition. The knowledge it holds is an invaluable reference for practicing skills and hand craft methods. Its chapters thoroughly discuss some of the essential building blocks of knowledge that are fundamental but may have been forgotten as equipment gets fancier and technology gets smarter. In short, this book was chosen for Legacy Edition printing because much of the basic skills and knowledge it contains has been forgotten or put to the wayside in trade for more modern conveniences and methods.

Although the editors at Doublebit Press are thrilled to have comfortable experiences in the woods and love our high-tech and light-weight equipment, we are also realizing that the basic skills taught by the old masters are more essential than ever as our culture becomes more and more hooked on digital stuff. We don't want to risk forgetting the important steps, skills, or building blocks involved with thriving in the outdoors. The Legacy Edition series represents the essential contributions to the American outdoors tradition by the great experts of outdoors life and traditional hand crafting.

With technology playing a major role in everyday life, sometimes we need to take a step back in time to find those basic building blocks used for gaining mastery – the things that we have luckily not completely lost and has been recorded in books over the last two centuries. These skills aren't forgotten, they've just been shelved. *It's time to unshelve them once again and reclaim the lost knowledge of self-sufficiency.*

Based on this commitment to preserving our outdoors and handcraft heritage, we have taken great pride in publishing this book as a complete original work. We hope it is worthy of both study and collection by outdoors folk in the modern era of outdoors and traditional skills life.

Unlike many other photocopy reproductions of classic books that are common on the market, this Legacy Edition does not simply place poor photography of old texts on our pages and use error-prone optical scanning or computer-generated text. We want our work to speak for itself, and reflect the quality demanded by our customers who spend their hard-earned money. With this in mind, each Legacy Edition book that has been chosen for publication is carefully remastered from original print books, *with the Doublebit Legacy Edition printed and laid out in the exact way that it was presented at its original publication.* We provide a beautiful, memorable experience that is as true to the original text as best as possible, but with the aid of modern technology to make as beautiful a reading experience as possible for books that are typically over a century old.

Because of its age and because it is presented in its original form, the book may contain misspellings, inking errors, and other print blemishes that were common for the age. However, these are exactly the things that we feel give the book its character, which we preserved in this Legacy Edition. During digitization, we ensured that each illustration in the text was clean and sharp with the least amount of loss from being copied and digitized as possible. Full-page plate illustrations are presented as they were found, often including the extra blank page that was often behind a plate. For the covers, we use the original cover design to give the book its original feel. We are sure you'll appreciate the fine touches and attention to detail that your Legacy Edition has to offer.

For outdoors enthusiasts who demand the best from their equipment, this Doublebit Press Legacy Edition reprint was made with you in mind. Both important and minor details have equally both been accounted for by our publishing staff, down to the cover, font, layout, and images. It is the goal of Doublebit Legacy Edition series to preserve outdoors heritage, but also be cherished as collectible pieces, worthy of collection in any outdoorsperson's library and that can be passed to future generations.

Every book selected to be in this series offers unique views and instruction on important skills, advice, tips, tidbits, anecdotes, stories, and experiences that will enrichen the repertoire of any person who enjoys escaping the city and finding their way to the trails of the wilds. To learn the most basic building blocks of outdoors life leads to mastery of all its aspects.

THREE BOOKS
IN ONE VOLUME

BOOK 1: THE USFS CHAIN SAW AND CROSSCUT SAW USE TRAINING COURSE

BOOK 2: THE CROSSCUT SAW MANUAL

BOOK 3: SAWS THAT SING

USDA

United States
Department of
Agriculture

Forest Service

Technology &
Development
Program

6700 Safety & Health
December 2006
0667-2805-MTDC

Chain Saw
and Crosscut Saw
Training Course

Student's Guidebook

2006 Edition

MISSOULA TECHNOLOGY AND DEVELOPMENT CENTER

Acknowledgments

Thanks to the following individuals for their contributions to this training course:

R.C. Carroll (retired)—Chapter 4
Paul Chamberlin—Chapter 2
David E. Michael—Chapter 5
Winston Rall—Chapter 3

and MTDC staff:
Ian Grob, Gary Hoshide, Bert Lindler, Ted J. Cote, Sara Lustgraaf (retired), Deb Mucci

Contents

Contents

Chapter 1—Course Information (Suggested time: 2 hours)

A Note to the Instructor... The *Chain Saw and Crosscut Saw Training Course* is a 16- to 32-hour course for basic to intermediate chain saw and crosscut saw users. The course is designed to provide the technical knowledge and skills that employees or volunteers will need to use these tools safely.

For specific needs, such as small limbing and bucking projects by volunteers, portions of the course can be adapted and modified. The reduced course can then be taught in less time. Certification is still required. Remem-ber, the primary objective is to provide class-room and field training for anyone using chain saws and crosscut saws.

The materials, such as the *Chain Saw and Crosscut Saw Training Course Instructor's Guidebook* (0667-2804-MTDC) and the *Chain Saw and Crosscut Saw Training Course Student's Guidebook* (0667-2805-MTDC), are designed to be presented in a variety of ways: through lectures, discussions, audiovisual aids, classroom exer-cises, and field training.

Instructors shall comply with the procedures outlined for the field training and evaluation (chapter 6) of this training course.

Because of the different types of vegetation that chain saw and crosscut sawyers experience when working throughout the United States, instructors should supply additional materials, such as slides showing vegetation typical in the area and regional statistics regarding ac-cidents and safety trends.

Course Instructions

The course instructions contain information essential to the instructor. The *Health and Safety Code Handbook* refers to the 1999 version. The instructor must read the course instructions and be thoroughly familiar with all procedures and material before teaching the course. Each regional safety manager or chain saw/crosscut saw program manager should develop a list of local experts, technical specialists, and professional consultants to assist during training, as needed.

Instructor Prerequisites

The instructors for this course shall follow established regional policies for saw training. Instructors shall conduct the course safely, ensuring that all agency and U.S. Department of Labor Occupational Safety and Health Administration (OSHA) regulations are obeyed. Instructors shall be certified by their forests as skilled and knowledgeable in the area they are instructing, as outlined in this course. Instructors must have successfully completed an instructor-training course that emphasizes adult education teaching skills. Instructors shall have a demonstrated ability to instruct sawyers and to work with chain saws or crosscut saws. They should display a positive attitude and have the ability to communicate with large or small diverse groups.

Student Target Group

Employees who will be using chain saws or crosscut saws for project or field work.

Student Prerequisites

All students should be certified in basic first aid and CPR. They should have bloodborne pathogen training as well as hazardous materials communication training. Individ-uals who will be using chain saws shall be in a hearing conservation program for employees exposed to noise that equals or exceeds an 8-hour time-weighted average of 85 decibels (*Health and Safety Code Handbook* sec-tion 21.13).

Personal Protective Equipment

Each student shall have the following personal protective equipment and clothing (PPE) for any field training sessions:

- Forest Service-approved hardhat (full brim or cap style).
- Wrap-around eye protection (safety glasses or shield).
- Hearing protection (plugs or muffs, rated for 85 decibels and higher, for chain saw use only).
- Long-sleeved shirt (optional for crosscut saw use).
- Gloves (slip-resistant, appropriate for the weather conditions). Gloves shall be cut-resistant for chain filing.
- Trousers (loose fitting, without a solid hem, or that can be tucked into boots). Do not cut fire pants and allow them to ravel (stag).
- Chain saw chaps (recommended to overlap boots by at least 2 inches, for chain saw use only). Only saw chaps provided by the General Services Administration meeting the most current Forest Service specifications (6170–4) are approved for purchase and use.
- Heavy-duty, cut-resistant or leather, waterproof or water-repellent 8-inch-high, laced boots with non-skid soles and adequate ankle support; hard toes are optional (*Health and Safety Code Handbook*).
- Calked boots (recommended for wet, slippery conditions).
- Type IV first-aid kit. Employees should carry their own disposable gloves.

Course Objectives

Course objectives are stated in broad terms that define what students will be able to do after completing this course. Instructors shall emphasize the objectives.

Special unit objectives at the beginning of each unit define what students will be able to do after the unit has been completed.

Chapter 1—Course Information: Instructors will find instructions and information for conducting saw training.

Students will receive an overview of the chain saw/crosscut saw training program. Students will be provided information on the requirements for successful completion of the chain saw/crosscut saw training course.

Chapter 2—Safety Requirements: Students will be able to identify the elements in a job hazard analysis (JHA):
- The task or procedure to be accomplished.
- The hazards associated with the task or procedure.
- Abatement actions to eliminate or reduce the hazards.
- First-aid and emergency evacuation procedures.

Students will learn why personal protective equipment and clothing (PPE) is used, how it is used, and how it is maintained.

Students will be able to identify common safety mistakes made by chain saw and crosscut sawyers.

Chapter 3—Chain Saw Use and Maintenance: Students will be able to perform all field maintenance required to maintain a chain saw properly and operate it safely.

Chapter 4—Chain Saw Tasks and Techniques: Students will learn the importance of a thorough sizeup before limbing, brushing, slashing, bucking, and felling operations.

Students will understand the skills needed to operate a chain saw safely and efficiently.

Chapter 5—Crosscut Saw Tasks and Techniques: Students will understand different features of crosscut saws.

Students will understand how a saw cuts and how the saw's components function.

Students will test a crosscut saw, assess its performance, and recommend corrective measures.

Students will demonstrate knowledge of saw handles and their relationship to saw performance in various applications.

Students will understand the value of a good saw maintenance program.

Students will demonstrate how to sheathe and transport a saw.

Students will understand the importance of carefully selecting crosscut saw-related tools.

Students will obtain a working knowledge of the use of wedges in crosscut saw operations and how the use of wedges in crosscut saw applications differs from their use in chain saw applications.

Students will understand the proper preparation for bucking and felling. Students will be able to describe the hazards and binds associated with these operations and have working knowledge of the different types of cuts needed to perform these operations with a crosscut saw.

Chapter 6—Field Proficiency: Instructors will work with the students using the techniques from the course in a field environment. Students will perform limbing, bucking, and felling operations under the guidance of a qualified instructor/certifier and will be evaluated on their skill level.

Presentation Time: The *Chain Saw and Crosscut Saw Training Course* will require 16 to 32 hours for presentation. If material is added, more time will be required. Instructors must devote adequate time to prepare for their presentations. They should draw from their experience to add realism and credibility to the class material. If the course is being conducted solely for the use of crosscut saws or chain saws, the instructor will need to use the appropriate material from each chapter and cover the material that applies.

A streamlined course for specific needs, such as for volunteers on projects, can be taught in less time.

Classroom Requirements

The course is designed to be taught in the classroom and in the field. A classroom with audiovisual equipment will be needed to display training materials.

The classroom should:

- Have sufficient space, desks, tables, and equipment for the students.
- Have controlled lighting. Turn lights off and shade windows when showing audiovisual aids.
- Have good acoustics.
- Have good ventilation.
- Be in a quiet place that is not subject to interruptions.
- Have facilities such as break areas and rest rooms nearby.

Guidelines for Conducting Field Training and Evaluating Chain Saw and Crosscut Saw Operators

Chain saw and crosscut saw operation is an individual, skill-oriented task. During the field training and certification sessions, the number one concern is the safety of the participants and the public. Before field training, instructors are required to do a thorough job hazard analysis specific to the location and the types of training and evaluations that are scheduled. Chapter 6 has instructions for conducting the field portion of the course.

Other Training Materials

Glossary: A glossary of terms is included in the instructor's guidebook and the student's workbook.

Student Guidebook: The *Chain Saw and Crosscut Saw Training Course Student's Guidebook* (0667-2805-MTDC) is designed to be used with the lecture material and as a reference guide that the student will keep. Instructors will need to make enough copies of the workbook for the students in the class.

Additional Information for Sawyers: This section includes publications, videos, slide presentations, and Web sites that can supplement the course.

Forest Service Chain Saw and Crosscut Saw Program

Chapter objectives:
- Students will receive an overview of the chain saw and crosscut saw training course.
- Students will be provided with information on the requirements for successfully completing the chain saw and crosscut saw training course.

As Forest Service employees, you must be aware of all laws and standards that must be met before you operate a chain saw or crosscut saw.

Why do we have a national chain saw and crosscut saw program?

The national chain saw and crosscut saw program was developed to provide all sawyers a solid foundation for safe and efficient saw operation while felling, bucking, brushing, or limbing. This course will provide the skills to safely use chain saws and crosscut saws, and

serve as a refresher class for persons who have completed the training.

Safety is the most critical concern. Your safety, the safety of your coworkers, the safety of the public, and property protection should be a part of every plan you prepare and every action you take. Careful study and practice of saw operations will improve your abilities and help you identify your limitations.

This course is designed to train apprentice and intermediate sawyers to perform project work safely and efficiently. The chapters for both courses are summarized here:

The Chain Saw Course:
- Chapter 1 (classroom), *Course Information*
- Chapter 2 (classroom), *Safety Requirements*
- Chapter 3 (classroom), *Chain Saw Use and Maintenance*
- Chapter 4 (classroom), *Chain Saw Tasks and Techniques*
- Chapter 6 (field), *Field Proficiency*

The Crosscut Saw Course:
- Chapter 1 (classroom), *Course Information*
- Chapter 2 (classroom), *Safety Requirements*
- Chapter 5 (classroom), *Crosscut Saw Tasks and Techniques*
- Chapter 6 (field), *Field Proficiency*

Additional Information for Sawyers

Chain Saw and Crosscut Saw Documents

An Ax to Grind: A Practical Ax Manual (9923-2823P-MTDC), available at: *http://www.fs.fed.us/eng/t-d.php?link=pubs/htmlpubs/htm99232823/*. Missoula Technology and Development Center; 5785 Hwy. 10 West; Missoula, MT 59808-9361; 1999.

Falling and Bucking Training Standard and Fallers and Buckers' Handbook. Workers Compensation Board of British Columbia, Films and Posters Section; P.O. Box 5350; Vancouver, BC V6B5L5.

Oregon Maintenance and Safety Manual. Blount, Inc., Oregon Cutting Systems Division; 4909 SE. International Way; Portland, OR 97222-4679; (or) P.O. Box 22127; Portland, OR 97269-2127; 2006.

The Effect of Color on Temperatures Inside Hardhats (0651-2312-MTDC), available at: *http://www.fs.fed.us/eng/t-d.php?link=pubs/htmlpubs/htm06512312/.* Missoula Technology and Development Center; 5785 Hwy. 10 West; Missoula, MT 59808-9361; 2006.

Use the Right Citrus-Based Cleaning Products to Avoid Corrosion or Rust (0673-2319-MTDC), available at: *http://www.fs.fed.us/eng/t-d.php?link=pubs/htmlpubs/htm06732319/.* Missoula Technology and Development Center; 5785 Hwy. 10 West; Missoula, MT 59808-9361; 2006.

Your Hardhat: Inspection and Maintenance (0267-2331-MTDC), available at: *http://www.fs.fed.us/eng/t-d.php?link=pubs/htmlpubs/htm02672331/.* Missoula Technology and Development Center; 5785 Hwy. 10 West; Missoula, MT 59808-9361; 2002.

Chain Saw and Crosscut Saw Videos

An Ax to Grind (9923-2V01-MTDC). Missoula Technology and Development Center; 5785 Hwy. 10 West; Missoula, MT 59808-9361; 1999.

Be Smart—Be Sharp—Be Safe. Blount, Inc., Oregon Cutting Systems Division; 4909 SE. International Way; Portland, OR 97222-4679; (or) P.O. Box 22127; Portland, OR 97269-2127.

Chain Saw Documents

Inspecting and Repairing Your Chain Saw Chaps (0567-2816-MTDC), available at: *http://www.fs.fed.us/eng/t-d.php?link=pubs/htmlpubs/htm05672816/.* Missoula Technology and Development Center; 5785 Hwy. 10 West; Missoula, MT 59808-9361; 2005.

Inspecting, Cleaning, Repairing, and Retiring USDA Forest Service Chain Saw Chaps (0451-2324-MTDC), available at: *http://www.fs.fed.us/eng/t-d.php?link=pubs/htmlpubs/htm04512324/.* Missoula Technology and Development Center; 5785 Hwy. 10 West; Missoula, MT 59808-9361; 2004.

Chain Saw and Crosscut Saw PowerPoint Presentations

Situational Awareness Exercise for Chain Saw Sawyers (0667-2P01-MTDC) and *Situational Awareness Exercise for Crosscut Sawyers* (0667-2P02-MTDC). Missoula Technology and Development Center; 5785 Hwy. 10 West; Missoula, MT 59808-9361; 2006.

Chain Saw and Crosscut Saw Web Information

Up the Ante: A Hazard Tree Safety Initiative Web page at *http://www.fs.fed.us/r1/projects/haztree_index.shtml.*

Chain Saw Videos

Chain Maintenance Clinic: Oregon Cutting. Workers Compensation Board of British Columbia, Films and Posters Section; P.O. Box 5350; Vancouver, BC V6B5L5.

Principles of Safe, Correct, and Efficient Chain Saw Use in All Tree Felling Operations. D. Douglas Dent, Inc.; P.O. Box 1099; Prineville, OR 97754.

Chain Saw Courses

S-212 Wildland Fire Chain Saws. Training program. National Interagency Fire Center; 3833 South. Development Ave.; Boise, ID 83705.

Crosscut Saw Documents

Country Woodcraft. Langsner, Drew. ISBN No. 0-87857-200-7. Rodale Press; Emmaus, PA, 1978.

Crosscut Saw Guards (9723-2341-MTDC), available at: *http://www.fs.fed.us/eng/t-d.php?link=pubs/htmlpubs/htm97232341/*. Missoula Technology and Development Center; 5785 Hwy. 10 West; Missoula, MT 59808-9361; 1997.

Crosscut Saw Manual (7771-2508-MTDC), available at: *http://www.fs.fed.us/eng/t-d.php?link=pubs/htmlpubs/htm77712508/*. Revised December 2003. Missoula Technology and Development Center; 5785 Hwy. 10 West; Missoula, MT 59808-9361; 1977.

Crosscut Saw Reflections in the Pacific Northwest. Deaton, Jim. ISBN No. 0-87770-675-1. Ye Galleon Press; Fairfield, WA, 1998.

Crosscut Saw Tooth-Setting Tool (0223-2324-MTDC), available at: *http://www.fs.fed.us/eng/t-d.php?link=pubs/htmlpubs/htm02232324/*. Missoula Technology and Development Center; 5785 Hwy. 10 West; Missoula, MT 59808-9361; 2002.

Crosscut Saw Underbucking Tool (0223-2330-MTDC), available at: *http://www.fs.fed.us/eng/t-d.php?link=pubs/htmlpubs/htm02232330/*. Missoula Technology

and Development Center; 5785 Hwy. 10 West; Missoula, MT 59808-9361; 2002.

Field Tests Comparing Modern to Vintage Crosscut Saws (0523-2320-MTDC), available at: *http://www.fs.fed.us/eng/t-d.php?link=pubs/htmlpubs/htm05232320/*. Missoula Technology and Development Center; 5785 Hwy. 10 West; Missoula, MT 59808-9361; 2005.

Food and Agriculture Organization of the United Nations, Basic Technology in Forest Operations. FAO Forestry Paper 36. ISBN No. 92-5-101260-1, Rome, 1982.

Handtools for Trail Work: 2005 Edition (0523-2810-MTDC), available at: *http://www.fs.fed.us/eng/t-d.php?link=pubs/htmlpubs/htm05232810/*. Missoula Technology and Development Center; 5785 Hwy. 10 West; Missoula, MT 59808-9361; 2005.

Lightly on the Land: The SCA Trail-Building and Maintenance Manual. 2d ed. Birkby, Robert C., ISBN No. 0-89886-848-3. The Mountaineers, Seattle, WA, 2005.

Logging Principles & Practices in the U.S. and Canada. Brown, Nelson Courtland, John Wiley & Sons, Inc., 1934.

New Tools for Old Saws (0523-2815-MTDC), available at: *http://www.fs.fed.us/eng/t-d.php?link=pubs/htmlpubs/htm05232815/*. Missoula Technology and Development Center; 5785 Hwy. 10 West; Missoula, MT 59808-9361; 2005.

Northeastern Loggers' Handbook. Simmons, Fred C., USDA Agricultural Handbook No. 6, Northeast Forest Experiment Station, 1951.

Now You're Logging. Griffiths, Bus, ISBN No. 1-55017-072-4, Harbour Publishing, Madeira Park, BC, Canada, 1992.

Saws and Sawmills for Planters and Growers. Morris, John, ISBN No. 1-871315-11-5, Cranfield Press, Bedford, UK, 1991.

Saws That Sing: A Guide To Using Crosscut Saws (0423-2822-MTDC), available at: *http://www.fs.fed. us/eng/t-d.php?link=pubs/htmlpubs/htm04232822/.* Revised June 2007. Missoula Technology and Development Center; 5785 Hwy. 10 West; Missoula, MT 59808-9361; 2004.

Crosscut Saw Videos

Handtools for Trail Work. (9823-2V04-MTDC). Missoula Technology and Development Center; 5785 Hwy. 10 West; Missoula, MT 59808-9361; 1998.

Chapter 2—Safety Requirements (Suggested time: 2 hours)

Chapter Objectives: Students will be able to identify the elements in a job hazard analysis (JHA): the task or procedure to be accomplished, the hazards associated with the task or procedure, abatement actions to eliminate or reduce the hazards, first-aid and emergency evacuation procedures.

Students will learn why personal protective equipment (PPE) is used, how it is used, and how it is maintained.

Students will be able to identify common safety mistakes made by sawyers.

Job Hazard Analysis

A JHA (see sample at the end of this chapter) must be prepared (preferably with the assistance of the involved employees) before beginning any work project or activity. The JHA must:

- Identify the task or procedure to be accomplished. Such tasks could include limbing, bucking, or felling.
- Identify the hazards associated with the task or procedure. These hazards may include physical, biological, environmental, chemical, and other hazards. Examples of hazards include:
  —Physical hazards: Rocky terrain, slippery slopes.
  —Biological hazards: Insect bites, hantavirus.
  —Environmental hazards: Weather-related hazards such as hypothermia, wind, lightning.
  —Chemical hazards: Hazardous materials such as fuel mix for chain saws and oil for crosscut saws.
  —Other hazards: Personal security issues, public traffic, hunting seasons.
- Identify abatement actions that can eliminate or reduce hazards. Abatement actions in order of preference include:

1. Engineering controls: The most desirable method of abatement (such as ergonomic tools and equipment).
2. Substitution: Such as switching to high flashpoint, nontoxic solvents.
3. Administrative controls: Such as limiting exposure by reducing work schedules or establishing appropriate work practices and procedures.
4. PPE: The last method of abatement (such as using hearing protection when working with chain saws).

- Identify first-aid supplies and emergency evacuation procedures. In the event of an emergency evacuation, be prepared to provide the following information:
  —Nature of the accident or injury (avoid using the victim's name).
  —Type of assistance needed (ground, air, or water evacuation).
  —Location where the accident occurred and best access to the work site (road name or number).
  —Radio frequencies.
  —Contact person.
  —Local hazards to ground vehicles or aviation.
  —Weather conditions (windspeed and direction, visibility, temperature).
  —Topography.
  —Number of individuals to be transported.
  —Estimated weight of individuals for air or water evacuation.

First Aid

Refer to the *Health and Safety Code Handbook* chapter 20, sections 21.21 and 21.22, for information on handling a medical emergency. The onsite first-aid kit must have supplies that meet Occupational Safety and Health Administration (OSHA) specifications and requirements. A Type IV first-aid kit must be available as a minimum (General Services Administration national stock number NSN 6545-01-010-7754). A more complete kit meeting higher standards may be used.

Emergency Evacuation Plan

An emergency evacuation plan is essential for any field project, especially one involving chain saws and crosscut saws. All employees need to be proficient in using a radio. They need to know which frequencies to use and whom to contact in the event of an emergency. The latitude and longitude and/or the legal location for an emergency medical helispot shall be determined and included in the JHA before starting any work. The entire crew shall know where the helispot is located. The emergency evacuation plan needs to be updated when the work location changes.

The JHA and emergency evacuation plan shall be signed by employees, signifying that they have read and understood the contents, have received the required training, are qualified to perform the task or procedure, and will comply with all safety procedures.

A copy of the JHA, the bloodborne-pathogen exposure control plan, the material safety data sheets for products used on the work project or activity, and the emergency evacuation plan must be kept onsite during the project. The JHA can be reviewed and updated during tailgate safety sessions. These sessions take place before a new project or activity is begun, when changes are made (such as changing location, adding crewmembers, or changing job responsibilities), or whenever employees believe a session is needed. Topics often focus on the hazards associated with the job and methods to eliminate or abate them.

Personal Protective Equipment

Refer to the *Health and Safety Code Handbook* chapter 70, section 72 for items that must be included in the JHA.

PPE	Chain Saw Operations	Crosscut Saw Operations
Forest Service-approved hardhat	Full brim or cap style	Full brim or cap style
Wrap-around eye protection	Safety glasses or shield	Safety glasses or shield
Hearing protection	Plugs or muffs rated for 85 decibels and higher	Not required
Long-sleeved shirt	Required	Optional
Gloves	Slip-resistant, appropriate for the weather conditions, and shall be cut-resistant for chain filing	Slip-resistant, appropriate for the weather conditions
Trousers	Loose fitting, without a solid hem, or that can be tucked into boots. Do not cut fire pants and allow them to ravel (stag).	Loose fitting, without a solid hem, or that can be tucked into boots. Do not cut fire pants and allow them to ravel (stag).

Continued

PPE	Chain Saw Operations	Crosscut Saw Operations
Boots	Heavy-duty, cut-resistant or leather, waterproof or water-repellent, 8-inch-high, laced, with nonskid soles and adequate ankle support. Hard toes are optional (*Health and Safety Code Handbook*). Calked boots are recommended for wet, slippery conditions.	Heavy-duty, cut-resistant or leather, waterproof or water-repellent, 8-inch-high, laced, with nonskid soles and adequate ankle support. Hard toes are optional (*Health and Safety Code Handbook*). Calked boots are recommended for wet, slippery conditions.
Chain saw chaps	Must overlap boots by at least 2 inches. Only saw chaps provided by the General Services Administration meeting the most current Forest Service specifications (6170–4) are approved for purchase and use.	Optional
Type IV first-aid kit	Required. Employees should carry their own disposable gloves.	Required. Employees should carry their own disposable gloves.

PPE should be used with engineering controls, substitution, administrative controls, or a combination of those approaches. Relying on PPE alone is not adequate.

General requirements should be followed for assessing the head, eye, face, hand, and foot hazards of a work project or activity.

General Requirements—
• Select PPE based on hazards identified in the JHA.
  —PPE shall fit properly.
  —Defective, damaged, or unsanitary PPE shall not be used.
  —Supervisors shall assure the adequacy of PPE as well as its proper maintenance and sanitation.
• Each employee shall be trained to wear the PPE required by the JHA. Training shall include:
  —The required PPE and when and how it should be worn.
  —Proper care, maintenance, useful life, limitations, and disposal of PPE.
• Before performing any work project or activity requiring PPE, employees need to demonstrate an understanding of its proper use. Employees are accountable for accidents and injuries that result from failing to use or from misusing required PPE.
• Additional training may be necessary. Circumstances in which supervisors should provide additional training include:
  —Workplace changes that make earlier training obsolete.
  —Changes in the PPE to be used.
  —Evidence that an employee's knowledge or use of PPE is not adequate.

Specific Requirements—

- *Eye and face protection:* Appropriate protection (including side protection) is needed when employees are exposed to eye or face hazards such as flying particles, chemical gases or vapors, or potentially injurious light (such as ultraviolet light). Face shields can be used in saw operations in addition to safety glasses or safety goggles.

- *Noise protection:* To comply with 29 CFR 1910.95, employees need to be in a hearing conservation program and wear ear plugs or ear muffs or both when working with equipment louder than 85 decibels (*Health and Safety Code Handbook* chapter 20, section 21.13b).

- *Head protection:* All hardhats and helmets should be designed to provide protection from impact and penetration hazards from falling objects. Inspect shells daily for signs of dents, cracks, penetration, or any other damage that might compromise protection. Suspension systems, headbands, sweatbands, and any accessories also should be inspected daily.

- *Hand protection:* Ensure that hand protection protects employees from the specific hazards that will be encountered. Gloves often are relied on to prevent cuts, abrasions, burns, and skin contact with chemicals that can cause local or systemic problems (29 CFR 1910.138).

- *Foot protection:* Footwear designed to prevent injury from falling or rolling objects and from objects that could pierce the soles. Heavy-duty, cut-resistant or leather, waterproof or water-repellent, 8-inch-high, laced boots with nonskid soles and adequate ankle support are required for chain saw use.

- *Additional protection:* Saw chaps, saw shoulder pads, or other PPE that provide cut resistance or puncture protection.

How Chain Saw Chaps Protect the User

When a chain saw strikes chain saw chaps, Kevlar fibers are pulled into the chain saw's drive sprocket, slowing and quickly stopping the chain.

A back-coated nylon shell covers the Kevlar protective pad inside the chaps. The shell resists water, oil, and abrasions. The protective pad consists of five layers of Kevlar in the following order: woven Kevlar, felted Kevlar, woven Kevlar, woven Kevlar, and felted Kevlar. Kevlar is an aramid fiber similar to the Nomex material used in firefighter's clothing. Kevlar is more resistant to flame than Nomex. When chain saw chaps are exposed to temperatures higher than 500 degrees Fahrenheit, the nylon shell may melt, but the protective Kevlar pad will not burn.

Chain saw users shall wear chaps. Chain saw chaps need to be adjusted properly and worn snug to keep them positioned correctly on the legs. The chaps should provide coverage 2 inches below the boot tops. Proper fit and correct length maximize protection!

Chain Saw Chaps Specifications (6170-4)—The Forest Service has provided cut-resistant protective chaps for chain saw sawyers since 1965. Chain saw chaps have prevented thousands of serious injuries.

The protective pad in the original Forest Service chain saw chaps consisted of four layers of ballistic nylon. Tests of chain saw chaps conducted by the Missoula Technology and Development Center (MTDC) concluded that

Continued ⟳➤

four layers of ballistic nylon offered protection to a chain speed of 1,800 feet per minute without a cut through. In 1981 Forest Service chain saw chaps were redesigned to improve the level of protection to a chain speed of 2,500 feet per minute without a cut through. The weight of the chaps was reduced by 40 percent, making them more comfortable.

The center monitors chain saw injuries. Because chain saws require right-hand operation, the majority of chain contact injuries occur on the left leg. In 2000, the Forest Service chain saw chaps were redesigned. The new design provides protection to a chain speed of 3,200 feet per minute without a cut through and increases the area of coverage for the left side of the left leg by about 2½ inches, and for the left side of the right leg by about 1½ inches. The higher level of protection and larger area of protection increased the weight of each pair of chaps by 6 to 8 ounces, depending on the length (32, 36, or 40 inches). Only saw chaps provided by the General Services Administration that meet the most current Forest Service specifications (6170-4) are approved for purchase and use by Forest Service employees.

Inspection and Replacement

Chain saw chaps need to be inspected and replaced when appropriate. Replace chain saw chaps when:

- The outer shell has numerous holes and cuts. Holes in the outer shell allow bar oil to be deposited on the protective pad. The oil acts as an adhesive, preventing fibers in the pad from moving freely, decreasing the protection.
- Wood chips and sawdust are evident in the bottom of the chaps.
- Repairs have stitched through the protective pad. Machine or hand stitching the protective pad prevents the fibers from moving freely, decreasing the protection.
- Cleaning has been improper. Detergents with bleach additives decrease the protection.
- High-pressure washing has destroyed the protective pad.
- The chaps have a cut that is more than 1 inch long in the first layer of yellow Kevlar.

Caring for Chain Saw Chaps

Treat your chain saw chaps as a **CRITICAL** piece of safety equipment. Keep them as clean as possible. Appropriate and timely cleaning reduces the flammability of the chaps and keeps them from soiling your clothing. Do not use your chaps as a chain stop.

Use *Citrosqueeze*, a commercially available citrus-based cleaning product, to clean chain saw chaps. Citrosqueeze has been tested and approved by Dupont for cleaning Nomex and Kevlar. Do not machine wash or machine dry chain saw chaps.

Cleaning Chain Saw Chaps

Hose and brush off chain saw chaps to remove dirt. Citrosqueeze must be diluted before use.

Continued

- For light soiling, use a Citrosqueeze solution in a spray bottle (mix 1 part Citrosqueeze concentrate to 10 parts water). Spray solution on the area to be cleaned and brush the solution into the chaps with a bristle brush. Wait one-half hour, thoroughly rinse the chaps with cold water, and allow them to air dry.
- For heavy petroleum contamination, soak chain saw chaps in Citrosqueeze solution for a minimum of 4 hours, overnight if possible. Brush the chaps with a bristle brush, rinse them thoroughly with cold water, and allow them to air dry. Many pairs of chain saw chaps can be cleaned in a single soak tank. Use 10 to 15 gallons of solution in a soak tank.

A United States manufacturer for Citrosqueeze is:

Emco Industries
2590 Jason Court
Oceanside, CA 92054
Phone: 760-305-5561
Fax: 760-305-5562

Repairs

Clean all chaps before repairing them. Repair cuts and holes in the outer shell as soon as possible to prevent the protective Kevlar pad from becoming contaminated with bar oil and petroleum products.

When repairing damage to the chaps' nylon shell, use a commercially available product called *Seam Grip*. Seam Grip provides a flexible, waterproof, and abrasion-resistant patch that will prevent petroleum products from contaminating the protective Kevlar pad.

Remove chain saw chaps from service if they have a cut longer than 1 inch in the top layer of Kevlar.

To repair holes and tears in the nylon shell:
- Cut a piece of notebook or printer paper that extends about 2 inches beyond the edge of the damage.
- Slip the paper inside the hole or tear so the paper lies on top of the protective Kevlar pad.
- Lay the chaps on a flat, level surface and press the nylon shell onto the piece of paper.
- Squeeze Seam Grip onto the paper and onto the sides of the tear so there is good coverage on all sides of the tear or hole.
- Allow the patch to dry for at least 12 hours before using the chaps.

Seam Grip is available through outdoor retailers. To learn of retailers close to you, contact:

McNett Corp.
Box 996
Bellingham, WA 98227
Phone: 360-671-2227
Fax: 360-671-4521
Web site: *http://www.mcnett.com*

Situational Awareness

The situational awareness checklist can be used for self-assessment during sawing operations. It also can be used for discussions, tailgate safety sessions, or one-on-one problem solving (to overcome performance or skill deficiencies) in the field.

Checklist of Personal Safety Considerations and Attitude

- How do I feel about this sawing assignment?
- Am I exercising sound judgment and awareness?
- Is my attitude influencing me to go against my better judgment (gut feeling)?
- Is my mind on my work project or activity?
- Do I have self-confidence?
- Am I overconfident?
- Am I doing this against my will? (*Health and Safety Code Handbook*, chapter 20, section 22.48)
- Is peer pressure a factor?
- Am I professional enough to decline the assignment and ask for assistance?
- Do I have all of the required PPE and sawing equipment to do the job safely? Am I committed to using the PPE and equipment correctly?
- Am I complacent?
- Am I violating any safe operating procedures?
- Do I feel hurried or unusually stressed to get the tree on the ground or bucked?
- Have all options been considered and discussed with others?
- Am I in an unfamiliar environment and timber type?
- Do I watch out for my coworkers, contractors, and the public?

Evaluating the Complexity of the Assignment

The individual sawyer must determine the complexity of the assignment. The evaluation of the complexity of the assignment must be based on the individual sawyer's skill, knowledge, and an understanding of the sawyer's personal capabilities and limitations. The final decision to cut any tree is left up to the individual sawyer. You have the responsibility to say no and walk away from any sawing situation that is beyond your capabilities.

Once the specific situation has been assessed thoroughly, the decision to cut or not to cut will be determined by the following *Go, No-Go* process.

Deciding Whether To Cut a Tree

Go! I feel comfortable with the sawing situation—I will cut the tree.
No Go! I don't feel comfortable with the situation—I will walk away from the tree.

Never base your decision on what you think you *might* be able to do. Remember...your safety and the safety of your coworkers depends on the decisions you make.

Sample Job Hazard Analysis (Following pages)

U.S. Department of Agriculture Forest Service	1. WORK PROJECT/ACTIVITY	2. LOCATION	3. UNIT
	CHAIN SAW USE		FS-6700-7 (03/00)
JOB HAZARD ANALYSIS (JHA) References: FSH 6709.11 and 6709.12 (Instructions on reverse)	4. NAME OF ANALYST	5. JOB TITLE	6. DATE PREPARED

7. TASKS/PROCEDURES	8. HAZARDS	9. ABATEMENT ACTIONS (Engineering controls • substitution • administrative controls • PPE)
Chain Saw Operation		**Qualifications** • Current certification by a nationally recognized organization to render first aid and perform CPR. Partici-pation in an approved crosscut/chain saw program (Classroom and field training encompassing in part or in total a national training program, such as Wildland Fire Saws S-212). Supervisors—Ensure that saw operators receive training or retraining in first aid and CPR before certifications expire. Elements include: • Demonstration of sawing ability (to a certified operator or certified instructor) in functional areas. • Supervision by a certified instructor or certified operator of saw work by new operators. Supervisors—Monitor proficiency of sawyers to recognize the need for recertification (additional training) in less than 3 years. **Personal Protective Equipment (PPE)** Employees—Maintain PPE in a clean and fully functional condition. Required PPE: • Forest Service-approved hardhat. • Eye protection. • Hearing protection (85 dB and above). • Appropriate gloves (cut-resistant gloves for chain filing). • Long-sleeved shirt. • Chain saw chaps (Forest Service-approved, minimum of 2 inches boot overlap). • Heavy-duty, cut-resistant or leather, waterproof or water-repellent, 8-inch-high, laced boots with nonskid soles (hard toes are optional). • Fire shelter (wildfire and prescribed-burn assignments).
	Falling objects Flying or spraying objects Noise Sharp or pointed objects	Required chain saw features: • Throttle interlock. • Felling and bucking spikes for felling and bucking operations (full set of two). • Antivibration system. • Chain brake, fully functional. • Proper saw for the job, fully operational (full wraparound handle bar for felling operations is required, three-quarter handlebars are allowed for bucking and limbing only). • Proper bar length for the specific work project or activity. • Bow bars with top and bottom chain guards and stingers. • Chain, filed and maintained.
	Ergonomics, fatigue	General equipment: • Type IV first-aid kit. • Fire extinguisher. • Chain saw wrench. • Chain file with handle and guard. • Approved safety container for fuel. • Chain and bar oil container, clearly marked. • Proper wedges for the specific work project or activity (wooden wedges are not permitted). • Single-bit ax or maul, 3 to 5 pounds.

1. WORK PROJECT/ACTIVITY	2. LOCATION	3. UNIT
CHAIN SAW USE		FS-6700-7 (03/00)

U.S. Department of Agriculture
Forest Service

JOB HAZARD ANALYSIS (JHA)
References: FSH 6709.11 and 6709.12

4. NAME OF ANALYST	5. JOB TITLE	6. DATE PREPARED

7. TASKS/PROCEDURES	8. HAZARDS	9. ABATEMENT ACTIONS (Engineering controls • substitution • administrative controls • PPE)
Transporting the Saw	Walking	**Safety Practices** • Carry so the bar (teeth) point downhill and away from the body—cover the bar if carrying on your shoulder. Prevent injury from cutters, dogs, and muffler.
		• Shut down the saw when carrying farther than tree to tree, or when slippery surfaces or brush create additional hazards.
		• Activate the chain brake for shorter distances.
	Vehicle	• Do not carry saws or fuel (including empty fuel containers) in the passenger compartment.
		• Do not store fuel and food together.
Situational Awareness and Sizeup		Analyze the cutting area by considering;
		• Location of people, structures, powerlines, and other obstacles.
		• Roads and travel in the cutting area.
		• Topography and steep ground.
		• Nearby hazards such as trees, low-hanging and dead limbs, rocks, and brush.
		• Primary and secondary escape routes, and safety zones.
		• Wind direction and velocity, such as steady versus gusting and/or changing directions.
		• Tree species, both live and dead.
		• Diameter and height of trees.
		• Soundness of tree (split, lightning struck, broken-off top, rot, deterioration or physical damage to the root system, trunk, stem, limbs, or bark).
		• Lean direction.
		• Limb distribution.
		• Widow makers.
		• Spiked top.
		• Burning top.
		• Moisture (rain, snow, or ice).
	Slips, trips, and falls Walking surfaces	**Primary and Secondary Escape Routes, and Safety Zones** • Select and prepare the work area by clearing escape routes before starting the cut. • Walk out and check the intended lay of the tree thoroughly. • Plan the route from the stump to the safety zone, generally not less than 20 feet away; the farther the better.
	Falling objects	• If possible, stand behind another tree, preferably quartering back from the planned direction of fall. Wait and watch for at least 30 seconds after the tree hits the ground for branches and other broken tree parts to fall. The shielding tree should be sound and large enough to provide protection.
Bucking, Brushing, and Limbing	Kickback Bind Rolling logs	**Procedures** • Know where the tip of the bar is at all times. • Anticipate log tensions (binds) and compressions and plan mitigation. • Use wedges and/or the pie cut. Initiate the cut slowly to observe the bind.
	Tension	• Use caution when cutting limbs supporting the log off the ground. Do not saw from the downhill side. On steep ground, prevent bucked sections from rolling or sliding. Limb from the top of large logs. • Watch for and reduce tension carefully on saplings and limbs, using a series of small cuts on the tensioned side.

17

U.S. Department of Agriculture
Forest Service

1. WORK PROJECT/ACTIVITY
CHAIN SAW USE

2. LOCATION

3. UNIT

FS-6700-7 (03/00)

JOB HAZARD ANALYSIS (JHA)
References: FSH 6709.11 and 6709.12
(Instructions on reverse)

4. NAME OF ANALYST

5. JOB TITLE

6. DATE PREPARED

9. ABATEMENT ACTIONS (Engineering controls • substitution • administrative controls • PPE)

7. TASKS/PROCEDURES	8. HAZARDS	9. ABATEMENT ACTIONS
Felling	Human factors Other hazards (kickback, binds, rolling logs) Darkness	**Procedures** • Consider your mental and physical condition. • Saw from a safe standing height. Be alert and look up frequently. The undercut must be clean with an opening large enough to control the tree's fall nearly to the ground. Do not use corner or side cuts in hollow trees unless adequate holding wood can be maintained. Give a warning shout before beginning the back cut. Give another warning shout just before the tree falls. Insert a wedge into the back cut as soon as possible. In small-diameter trees, wedge into a corner cut. Do not cut off all of the holding wood. As the tree commits to the undercut, watch the top as you get away from the stump as quickly as possible. If the tree moves in a direction that compromises the primary escape route, use the secondary route. Do not leave a partially cut tree without marking it and warning others. When situations are deemed unsafe, use alternate methods or cancel the task. • No felling at night.
Handling Flammable and Combustible Liquids	Burns, flammability, and toxic fumes	**Safety Practices** • A hazard communication training program provides information related to general awareness, hazard chemical inventory, and MSDSs. • A hazardous-chemical inventory shall be maintained and shall be readily accessible to all employees. • Never handle hazardous chemicals that do not have an MSDS. An MSDS is required for each chemical used onsite and shall be readily accessible to employees at all times. **Transportation** • All containers (safety cans, drums, tanks, or tank trucks) used for transporting hazardous materials must be correctly labeled or placarded to ensure quick identification of the materials in an emergency. **Dispensing** • General Safety—All handling and dispensing of flammable liquids shall be done in a well-ventilated area free of sources of ignition, with bonding between the dispensing equipment and the container being filled.
Working Around Poisonous Plants	Accidental contact	**Procedures** • Teach all employees who are subject to exposure, especially those known to be highly sensitive, to recognize poisonous plants. When possible, do not assign allergic employees to jobs that expose them to poisonous plants. • Provide and apply a skin protectant or barrier cream. Fasten pant legs securely over boot tops (adhesive tape may be necessary). • Wear gloves and keep them away from the face and other exposed parts of the body. Do not touch skin with hands, clothes, or equipment that may have contacted poisonous plants. • Whenever the skin contacts a poisonous plant or noxious weed, wash the area with cold water within 1 to 3 minutes or as soon as possible. Use liberal amounts of water to ensure that all poisonous oils are washed off. While working around poisonous plants, do not wash with soap and/or hot water because they can remove natural protective oils from your skin. • Destroy poisonous plants around improved areas. • Avoid the smoke of burning poisonous plants. Inhaling this smoke can cause fever, malaise, respiratory problems, and severe rash. • Upon returning from the field, use rubbing alcohol to cleanse skin that contacted poisonous plants. • Clean tools with a citrus-based solvent before storing (use appropriate gloves and adequate ventilation). • Avoid handling contaminated clothes. Wash contaminated clothing separately from other clothes in hot water and detergent.

U.S. Department of Agriculture Forest Service	1. WORK PROJECT/ACTIVITY **CHAIN SAW USE**	2. LOCATION	3. UNIT
JOB HAZARD ANALYSIS (JHA) References: FSH 6709.11 and 6709.12 (Instructions on reverse)	4. NAME OF ANALYST	5. JOB TITLE	6. DATE PREPARED

FS-6700-7 (03/00)

9. ABATEMENT ACTIONS (Engineering controls • substitution • administrative controls • PPE)

7. TASKS/PROCEDURES	8. HAZARDS	
Working Around Insects	Ticks and mosquitoes	**Procedures** • Spray clothes with an insect repellant, as an additional barrier against ticks. Repellants, such as diethyl metatoloamide (DEET), do not kill ticks. Some sprays do contain permethrin, which kills ticks on contact. DEET should not be applied to Nomex, only to skin. Permethrin can be applied to Nomex, but not to skin. Always follow the manufacturer's application instructions for insect repellants and treatments. • Wear light-colored clothing that fits tightly at the wrists, ankles, and waist. Each outer garment should overlap the one above it. Cover trouser legs with high socks or boots and tuck shirttails inside trousers. • Search the body repeatedly (such as during rest periods and lunch), especially hairy regions and inside clothing, as ticks seldom attach themselves within the first few hours. • Remove ticks with fine-tipped tweezers or fingers. Grasp the tick as closely as possible to the point of attachment and pull straight up, applying gentle pressure. Wash the skin with soap and water, then cleanse with rubbing alcohol. Do not try to remove the tick by burning it with a match or covering it with chemical agents. If the head pulls off when the tick is being removed, or if the tick cannot be removed, seek medical attention. • Once the tick has been removed, place it in an empty container so it can be given to a physician if you experience a reaction. Record the dates of tick exposure and removal. An early warning sign to watch for is a large red spot on a tick bite. Reactions within 2 weeks may include fever, chills, headache, joint and muscle ache, significant fatigue, and facial paralysis. Seek medical attention promptly if you experience these reactions.

Emergency Evacuation Plan (see attached Emergency Evacuation Plan)		
10. LINE OFFICER SIGNATURE	11. TITLE	12. DATE

Field Site

EMERGENCY EVACUATION PLAN

Work project/activity: ___General saw use___
Location: _____
Legal description: _____

To prepare for an emergency that requires first aid and/or immediate evacuation of personnel due to serious injury, the following information shall be available to all crewmembers:

• Designated first-aid provider(s): at least one person on each crew should be designated to provide first aid.
• Communication procedures to follow in the event of an emergency.

19

(Suggested time: 2 hours)

Chapter objectives:

- Students will learn how to remove the bar and the chain, inspect them for damage and wear, and clean them.
- Students will learn how to remove and clean (or replace) the air and fuel filters.
- Students will learn how to inspect the power head for loose bolts and damage.
- Students will learn how to replace the bar and the chain.
- Students will learn how to file the chain.

Chain Saw Operation

The bar and chain are the most important parts of your chain saw. A sharp chain produces shavings that fall to the ground away from the power head. A clean bar in good condition guides the chain through the cut, making a straight, true cut.

A dull chain produces sawdust that gets sucked into the air filter, reducing power by limiting the airflow to the power head. A dull chain does not allow the saw to cut smoothly and puts unnecessary strain on the power head. The sawyer is forced to saw into the cut, increasing the stress on the power head. An improperly maintained bar and chain will damage the chain saw.

As the sawyer works harder to make the saw cut, the sawyer may become fatigued, increasing the risk of accident or injury. A dull chain also increases the risk of kickback.

The primary purpose of the chain saw and crosscut saw training and certification program is to provide for the safety of all employees who operate saws. Selecting the proper chain is important to the safe operation of a chain saw.

Chain Saw Components

Saw chain—The three most common types of cutter teeth used by the Forest Service are chipper, chisel, and semichisel. Saw chain is made up of several parts that work together and must be maintained properly for maximum performance and safety.

The cutter is the part of the saw chain that does the cutting. The saw chain has left- and right-hand cutters so that the saw chain will cut evenly through the wood.

The depth gauge (referred to as a raker in some parts of the country) determines the depth of the cut (figure 3-1).

Figure 3-1—The depth gauge is the part of the tooth used to set the thickness of the shaving.—Oregon Maintenance and Safety Manual, *permission by Blount, Inc.*

The three basic types of cutters include:

Chipper: The most versatile cutter type. Chipper chain (figure 3-2) is the easiest to file and will tolerate the most dirt and dust. Chipper chain cuts smoothly and is well suited for many Forest Service chain saw operations.

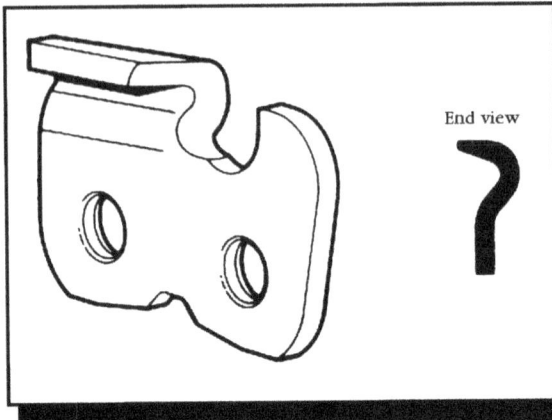

Figure 3-2—The chipper is the most versatile cutter type. Chipper chain is easy to file, will tolerate the most dirt, and can be used for many types of sawing operations.—Oregon Maintenance and Safety Manual, *permission by Blount, Inc.*

Chisel (figure 3-3): The most aggressive cutter type. It is designed for production timber felling and should be used only by experienced sawyers. Square-ground chisel

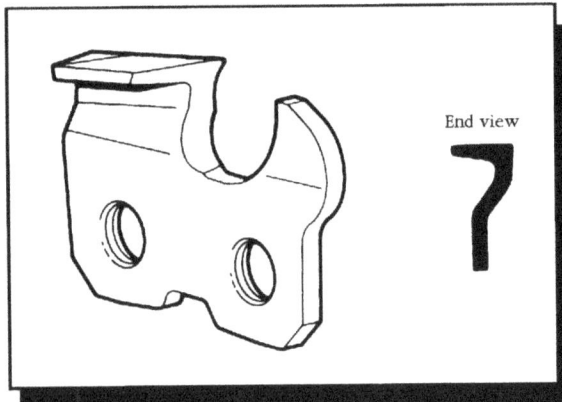

Figure 3-3—The chisel is the most aggressive cutter type. Chisel chain should be used only by experienced sawyers.—Oregon Maintenance and Safety Manual, *permission by Blount, Inc.*

chain requires a file that fits the square shape of the cutting edge. It is more difficult to file than other types of chain. No file guide is available. Round-ground chisel chain may be filed with a round file and file guide. All chisel chain dulls very quickly when it is exposed to dirt or dust. It is not recommended for brushing or limbing because of the potential for kickback.

Semichisel (figure 3-4): A less aggressive cutter type than chisel. A round file is used with a file guide when filing semichisel chain. The semichisel cutter is more tolerant of dirt and dust and stays sharp longer than the other cutters.

Low-kickback chain is the most desirable chain for training inexperienced sawyers. The chain cuts smoothly and is ideal for cutting brush, small-diameter material, dimensional lumber, house logs, and other materials that normally aren't cut with chain saws. Low kickback chain is available with chipper, chisel, and semichisel cutters.

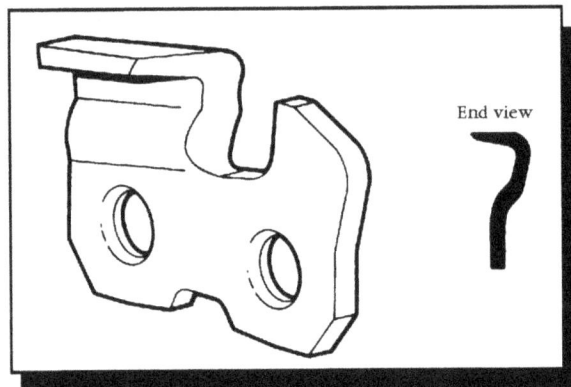

Figure 3-4—The semichisel cutter is less aggressive than the chisel cutter, will tolerate some dirt, and stays sharp longer than the chisel and the chipper cutters.—Oregon Maintenance and Safety Manual, *permission by Blount, Inc.*

Parts of the chain (figure 3-5).

Figure 3-5—Parts of the chain.—Oregon Maintenance and Safety Manual, *permission by Blount, Inc.*

Tie strap: Holds the parts of the saw chain together.

Drive link: Fits in the bar groove so the bar can guide the chain and into the chain sprocket so the power head can drive the chain around the bar.

Cutter sequences (figure 3-6).

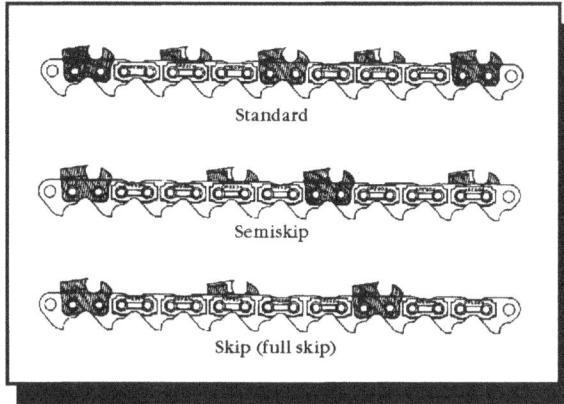

Figure 3-6—The cutter sequences for three types of chains: standard, semiskip, and skip (full skip).—Oregon Maintenance and Safety Manual, *permission by Blount, Inc.*

Standard: This chain has a cutter sequence of: left-hand cutter, tie strap, right-hand cutter, tie strap, left-hand cutter, tie strap, right-hand cutter—for the length of the chain.

Semiskip: This chain has a cutter sequence of: left-hand cutter, two tie straps, right-hand cutter, one tie strap, left-hand cutter, two tie straps, right-hand cutter, one tie strap, left-hand cutter—for the length of the chain.

Skip or full skip: This chain has a cutter sequence of: left-hand cutter, two tie straps, right-hand cutter, two tie straps—for the length of the chain.

Guide bar—The guide bar supports and guides the saw chain.

The most common types of bars are solid nose and sprocket nose (figure 3-7). A sprocket nose bar has a

sprocket in the nose to reduce drag and help the chain move freely around the bar. Generally, a solid nose bar is found on small saws. The bar is solid without a sprocket.

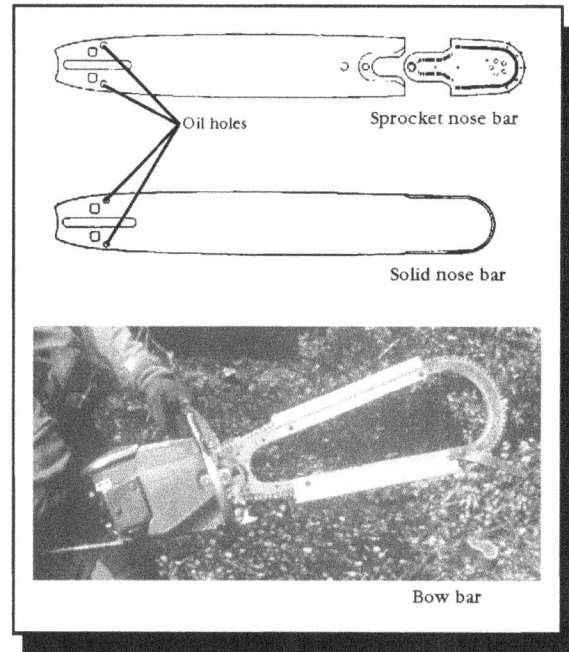

Figure 3-7—The three most common types of guide bars.—Oregon Maintenance and Safety Manual, *permission by Blount, Inc.*

Parts of a chain saw—
- *Bar studs*—Hold the bar and chain sprocket cover in place.
- *Front and side chain tensioner*—Moves the guide bar to maintain proper tension on the saw chain.
- *Chain sprocket*—The toothed wheel that drives the saw chain.
- *Chain brake*—Stops the saw chain if it is activated by the sawyer's hand or by inertia (during kickback).
- *Clutch*—Couples the engine to the chain sprocket when the engine is accelerated above idle speed.
- *Chain catcher*—Helps reduce the risk of the saw chain contacting the sawyer if the chain breaks or if the chain is thrown off the bar.
- *Starter grip*—A rubber or plastic handle attached to the starter pull rope.

- *Bumper spikes (dogs)*—Hold the saw steady against wood.
- *Handlebar*—Used to hold the front of the saw.
- *Hand guard*—Activates the chain brake and prevents the sawyer's hand from contacting the chain.
- *Gunning marks*—Used to determine the planned direction of the tree's fall based on the undercut.
- *Throttle handle*—Used to hold the rear of the saw.
- *Throttle trigger*—Controls the speed of the engine.
- *Throttle interlock*—Prevents the throttle from being activated unless it is depressed.
- *On/off switch*—Turns the saw on and off.
- *Choke*—Used for starting a cold saw.
- *Air filter cover*—Holds the air filter in place and covers the carburetor.
- *Air filter*—Prevents dirt, dust, and sawdust from entering the carburetor.
- *Fuel filter*—Prevents dirt and other contaminants from entering the saw's carburetor (not shown).
- *Oil and fuel caps*—Seal the oil and fuel tanks.

- *Muffler*—Reduces exhaust noise.
- *Spark arrester*—Prevents hot sparks from leaving the muffler.
- *Spark plug*—Ignites fuel in the power head.
- *Carburetor adjustments*—Chain saws have a two-stage carburetor that provides fuel to the engine in any position that a saw may be held. The carburetor has three adjustments:
  —Idle speed sets the speed at which the saw's engine will run by itself.
  —Low-end speed controls the mixture of air and fuel on the first half of the throttle.
  —High-end speed controls the mixture of air and fuel on the second half of the throttle.
  The high- and low-end adjustments should be made by a qualified saw mechanic. Improper adjustment can result in poor operation or severely damage the chain saw.
  The idle adjustment may need to be adjusted in the field. Before adjusting the idle, be sure that the air

---

Parts of a Chain Saw

1	Saw chain	9	Starter grip	18	Choke
2	Guide bar	10	Bumper spikes (dogs)	19	Air filter cover
3	Bar studs	11	Handlebar	20	Air filter
4	Front and side chain tensioners	12	Hand guard	21	Oil and fuel caps
5	Chain sprocket	13	Gunning marks	22	Muffler
6	Chain brake	14	Throttle handle	23	Spark arrester
7	Clutch	15	Throttle trigger	24	Spark plug
8	Chain catcher	16	Throttle interlock	25	Carburetor adjustments
		17	On/off switch		

—From Chain Safety Manual, *permission by Stihl, Inc.*

filter and fuel filter are clean and that you are using the right fuel mixture. Dirty filters or improper fuel mixtures affect the idle speed.

Newer saws designed to meet the U.S. Environmental Protection Agency (EPA) air quality standards may not have all three adjustments.

• *Mounts or antivibration system*—Buffers between the engine and the handles that reduce vibrations to the sawyer's hands (not shown).

Guide Bar Maintenance

Most guide bar problems develop in the bar rails and are caused by:

• Incorrect chain tension
• Lack of lubrication
• Improper cutting techniques
• Normal wear

Look for several rail conditions (figure 3-8) when performing daily maintenance on your saw. These conditions can be corrected if they are caught early. If they are ignored, they will destroy the bar or lead to cutting problems. For instance, it may not be possible to cut straight with the saw or to match cuts on larger material. In addition, the chain may be thrown because the chain tension is harder to control.

• Rails are worn down and the groove becomes shallow. If the groove is too shallow and the tie straps do not touch the rails, replace the bar.
• The outside edges of the rails develop wire edges. Use a flat file to remove them.
• The rail is worn low on one side. This causes the chain to cut at an angle. The bar will have to be ground on a specialized bar grinder. You may need to take the bar to a dealer or to a trained saw mechanic if your unit doesn't have a specialized bar grinder.

• The rails show blue discoloration along the bar or at the tip of the sprocket nose. This discoloration is caused by lack of lubrication, by poor cutting methods that push the drive links to the side, by a chain that is too tight, or by a dull or improperly filed chain. Blue spots are caused by excess heat. The spots are soft and will wear rapidly: you will need to replace the bar.

Figure 3-8—Correcting these rail conditions will prevent damage to the bar and cutting problems.—Oregon Maintenance and Safety Manual, *permission by Blount, Inc.*

• The bar shows excessive wear only behind the nose on solid nose bars or behind the sprocket on sprocket nose bars. This wear can be caused by heavy use near the nose of the bar (such as limbing) or by a chain that is too loose. You can reduce this wear by periodically turning the bar over. If wear becomes extensive, you may need to replace the bar.

- The bar is bent. This can be caused by improper cutting techniques, getting the saw pinched or bound in the cut, or improper transportation (such as carrying a saw loose in the bed of a pickup). Some bars can be straightened at a shop that has the proper equipment.

The condition of the guide bar has as much to do with the performance of your chain saw as the condition of the chain. The bar and the chain work together. When both are in proper condition, the chain saw does the work. All you have to do is guide it.

Chain Tension

Remember three basic rules for tensioning a saw chain:

- Turn the saw off!
- Wear protective gloves.
- Wait until the bar and chain have cooled before adjusting the tension.

Heat causes the bar and chain to expand when the chain saw is being used. If the tension is set while the chain is hot, the chain will be too tight when it cools. Tension that is set too tight can damage the bar and chain. To adjust the chain tension on a solid nose bar:

- Loosen the bar nuts on the side of the saw.
- Pull the nose of the bar up and keep the nose up as you adjust the tension.
- Turn your saw's adjustment screw until the bottoms of the lowest tie straps and cutters just touch the bottom of the bar.
- Still holding the nose up, tighten the rear bar nut, then the front bar nut.
- While wearing gloves, pull the chain along the top of the bar several times from the engine to the tip. The chain should feel snug, but pull freely.

The tension must be tighter on a sprocket nose bar than on a solid nose bar. To adjust the tension on a sprocket nose bar:

- Loosen the bar nuts on the side of the saw.
- Pull the nose of the bar up and keep the nose up as you adjust the tension.
- Turn your saw's adjustment screw until the bottoms of the lowest tie straps and cutters *solidly* contact the bottom of the bar.
- While wearing gloves, pull the chain along the top of the bar several times from the engine to the tip. The chain should feel snug, but still pull freely.

Daily Saw Maintenance

As the chain goes around the bar, it wears the bar and the chain. Because the bar is made of softer metal, the bar wears more than the chain. Generally, one rail will wear more than the other, causing the saw to cut at an angle if the bar and the chain are not maintained properly.

Chain saws have a chain oiler to minimize wear and prolong the life of the bar and chain. The oiler provides oil through a small hole in the bar that lines up with the oiler on the power head.

As oil is pumped through the oil hole, the chain carries it around the bar, lubricating the top, bottom, and roller tip. During operation, debris begins to build up in the chain groove. If the groove is not cleaned, oil cannot lubricate the entire bar, causing excessive wear and damage. If the oiler is properly adjusted, a full tank of gas will run dry before the oil tank is empty. As a general rule, a tank of oil should last as long as or longer than a tank of gas.

Clean and rotate the bar each time you file the chain or at least once a day. Be sure to clean the bar after filing the chain because the filings act as an abrasive, increasing the wear on the bar.

Cleaning Exercise—

Remove the bar and chain for inspection and cleaning.

- Check the bar for wear. Look for uneven rails, flared edges, cracks, and other damage that would require the bar to be repaired or serviced.
- Clean the chain groove and oil holes. The proper method for cleaning the chain groove is to start at the tip with the bar tool and clean toward the base, moving debris away from the roller tip. Be sure that the oil holes are clean.
- The sprocket nose (roller tip) should spin freely.
- Grease the roller tip.

Remove and clean the air filter. Never use an air hose to blow out the air filter.

- Take care not to damage the filter. Gently tap the filter against another surface. Don't rub or scrape it. Do not clean the filter with saw fuel. A damaged air filter can allow dust and debris into the engine, causing excessive wear and other problems.
- Follow the manufacturer's recommendations (found in the instruction manual) for cleaning the air filter and determining whether it needs to be replaced. A dirty or plugged air filter reduces the power and performance and may cause other seemingly unrelated problems.

Check the muffler and spark arrester. Replace the screen if it has any holes.

Remove the spark plug.

- Check for fouling.
- The tip of the plug should be beige, not black.
- The plug should be dry.
- Check the plug weekly when the saw is in frequent use.

Inspect the power head for loose bolts and damage.

- Tighten the bolts or repair the power head, if needed.
- Check the handlebars for loose bolts or cracks.
- Check the bumper spikes (dogs) for loose or bent bolts.
- Check the mounts. They are the antivibration system. Look for cracks in the rubber. Excessive movement of the engine or a loose feeling when the saw is held by the handles and shaken indicate that the mounts may be broken or that they need tightening.

Replace the bar and chain.

- Rotate the bar so it wears evenly.
- Check for proper alignment of the bar with the bar studs, adjuster, and oiler.
- Check the chain tension. The chain should be adjusted so that it doesn't hang from the bar but still turns freely.
- Check the chain brake to make sure it's operating properly.

Chain Maintenance

Chain maintenance is crucial to the performance of any chain saw. Before beginning any work assignment, follow four basic rules to maintain the saw chain for top performance and safe operation.

1. Your chain must be sharp. When it is, the chain does the work. When the chain is dull, you do the work, making you fatigued and increasing the wear on the bar and chain.
2. Your depth gauges must be set correctly. The gauges' depths and shapes are critical to the saw's performance and your safety.
3. Your chain must be correctly tensioned. More bar and chain problems are caused by incorrect chain tension than by any other single problem.
4. Your chain must be well lubricated. Your bar, chain, and roller tip need a steady supply of oil. Otherwise, your bar and chain will be subject to excessive wear and damage.

Several conditions can increase the chain's potential for kickback, the risk that the chain might be thrown or broken, or the risk of other hazards. Look for these conditions when inspecting your chain saw:

- Loose chain tension
- Incorrect chain angles (generally caused by improper filing)
- Dull chain
- Alteration of chain features designed to reduce kickback
- Incorrect depth gauge settings (generally too deep)
- Improper shape of depth gauges (rakers)after filing
- Incorrectly installed chain parts
- Loose rivets, or cracks and breaks in any part of the chain

Chain Filing

This section focuses on chain filing with a round file and a clamp-on (hand-held) file guide that clamps on the file, sometimes called a file holder. Using these files is the least complicated, least expensive, and most efficient

way to file saw chain by hand in the field. Select a file that is the proper diameter for the saw chain.

After the saw chain has been hand filed a few times, it should be ground on a chain grinder to restore angles that may have changed during hand filing and to grind all cutters to the same length.

Understanding how a cutter works will help you see why proper chain maintenance is so important.

The depth gauge rides on the wood and controls the depth at which the cutting corner bites into the wood (figure 3–9).

The cutting corner and side plate sever the wood fibers across the cross grain.

The top-plate cutting angle chisels out the severed wood fibers, lifting them from the kerf.

Three angles must be maintained when filing or grinding a saw chain (figure 3–10). A clamp-on file guide maintains these angles. The angles may vary on different types of saw chains.

Figure 3–9—The depth gauge controls the depth at which a tooth's cutting corner bites into the wood.— Oregon Maintenance and Safety Manual, *permission by Blount, Inc.*

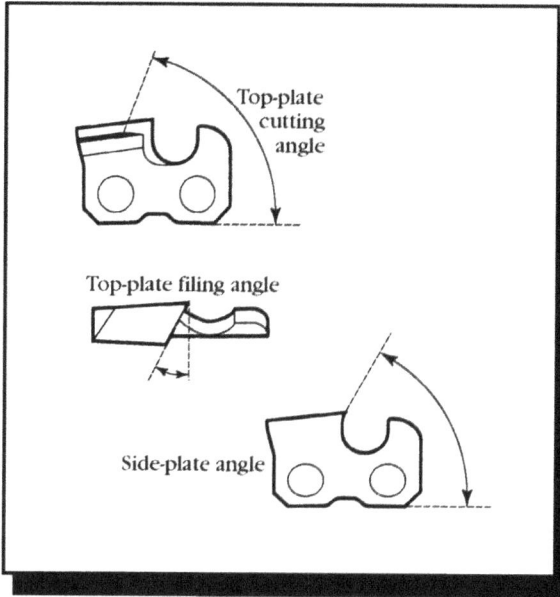

Figure 3-10—Maintain the top-plate cutting angle, top-plate filing angle, and side-plate angle.—Oregon Maintenance and Safety Manual. *permission by Blount, Inc.*

Sharpening Cutters With a Round File—Be sure that the chain is tensioned properly. The file must be held at least one-fifth of the file's diameter above the cutter's top plate (figure 3-11). The clamp-on file guide positions the file for you.

Figure 3-11—Hold the file at least one-fifth of the file's diameter above the cutter's top plate.—Oregon Maintenance and Safety Manual, *permission by Blount, Inc.*

Maintain the correct top plate angle (as marked on the file guide) by keeping the filing angle parallel with the chain (figure 3-12).

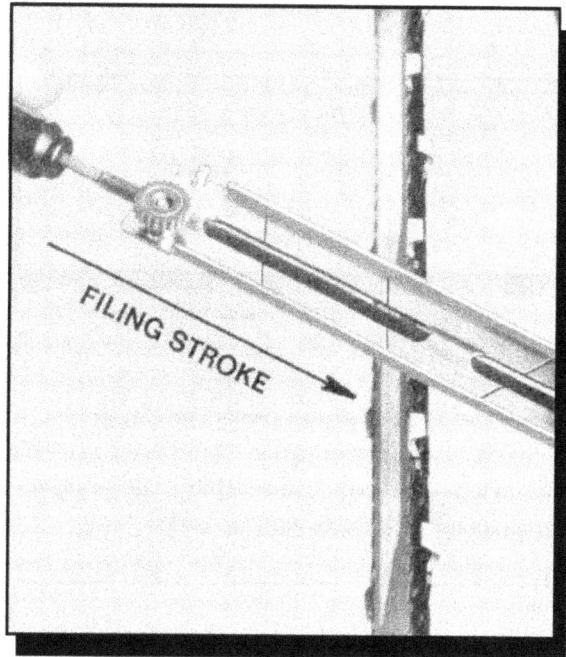

Figure 3-12—The correct top-plate angle is marked on the file guide.—Oregon Maintenance and Safety Manual, *permission by Blount, Inc.*

Sharpen cutters on one side of the chain first, filing from the inside of each cutter to the outside. Turn the saw around and repeat the process for the remaining side (figure 3-13).

Figure 3-13—Sharpen the cutters on one side of the chain before turning the saw around to sharpen the other side.—Oregon Maintenance and Safety Manual, *permission by Blount, Inc.*

If the chrome surface of the top or side plates has been chipped, file until the chip has been removed from the chrome surface.

Keep the length of all cutters equal (figure 3-14).

Figure 3-14—All cutters should be the same length.—Oregon Maintenance and Safety Manual, *permission by Blount, Inc.*

How To Set Depth Gauges—Use a depth-gauge tool with the correct built-in setting for the chain. Place the tool on top of the chain so one depth gauge protrudes through the slot in the tool (figure 3-15).

Figure 3-15—A depth gauge protrudes through the slot in the depth-gauge tool.—Oregon Maintenance and Safety Manual, *permission by Blount, Inc.*

If the depth gauge extends above the slot, use a flat file to file the depth gauge level with the top of the tool. Never file a depth gauge lower than the top of the tool.

After lowering a depth gauge, round off its leading edge (figure 3-16).

Figure 3-16—After lowering a depth gauge, always round off its leading edge.—Oregon Maintenance and Safety Manual, *permission by Blount, Inc.*

Chain Filing Exercise—

- Wear appropriate gloves for hand protection as described in your JHA.
- Make sure the chain is tensioned properly.
- Maintain the correct top-plate angle (as marked on the file guide) by keeping the filing angle parallel with the chain.
- File one side of the chain, then the other.
- Keep the length of all cutters equal.
- Set depth gauges with a depth-gauge tool.

Saw Transportation

Saws must be transported in a way that protects them from being damaged, from injuring people, and from damaging property and equipment.

Transporting Chain Saws in a Vehicle—
- Keep the bar and chain covered with a chain guard.
- Properly secure the chain saw to prevent it from being damaged and to prevent fuel from spilling.
- Never transport a chain saw or fuel in a vehicle's passenger compartment.

Transporting Chain Saws by Hand—The muffler and power head can reach extremely high temperatures. Avoid these areas when carrying a saw that has been used recently.

- When carrying the saw for short distances, set the saw at idle speed and set the chain brake.
- When carrying the saw farther than from tree to tree, or in hazardous conditions (such as slippery surfaces or heavy underbrush), and in all cases if the saw is carried more than 50 feet, the saw shall be shut off and carried in a way that prevents the chain, muffler, and bumper spikes (dogs) from contacting your body.
- When carrying the saw on your shoulder, take extra care because of the sharpness of the chain and bumper spikes (dogs). A long-sleeved shirt, gloves, and a shoulder pad must be worn. The bar, chain, and bumper spikes (dogs) should be covered, preferably with a manufactured bar and chain cover. Chain saw chaps can be used to cover the bumper spikes (dogs).

Safe Chain Saw Use

The methods to safely start and operate a saw can vary with the make and model.

Starting Procedures—

Take extra care when starting your chain saw. Because you won't have both hands on the saw, you will need to be more careful to maintain complete control. Remember that on/off switches may vary with different makes of saws.

- Ensure that appropriate PPE is available and is worn correctly.
- Maintain a secure grip on the saw at all times.
- Always start the saw with the chain brake engaged.
- Start the saw on the ground or where it is supported firmly with the nose of the saw bar over a stump or log. To successfully start a cold saw, "feather" the throttle trigger. Avoid engaging the throttle lock or the fast idle position of the on/off switch.
- Make sure that the saw's bar and chain do not contact anything.

- "Drop starting" a chain saw is strictly forbidden. Do not drop start a chain saw. This is the most dangerous method of starting a saw because you have no control of the saw.

Starting the Chain Saw on the Ground—
- Set the chain brake.
- Place the saw on firm ground in an open area (figure 3-17).
- Grip the front handlebar firmly with your less dominant hand.
- Pull the starting rope with your dominant hand until you feel resistance.
- Give a strong, brisk pull. Gradually return the starting rope to the saw housing. Do NOT allow the starting rope to snap back.

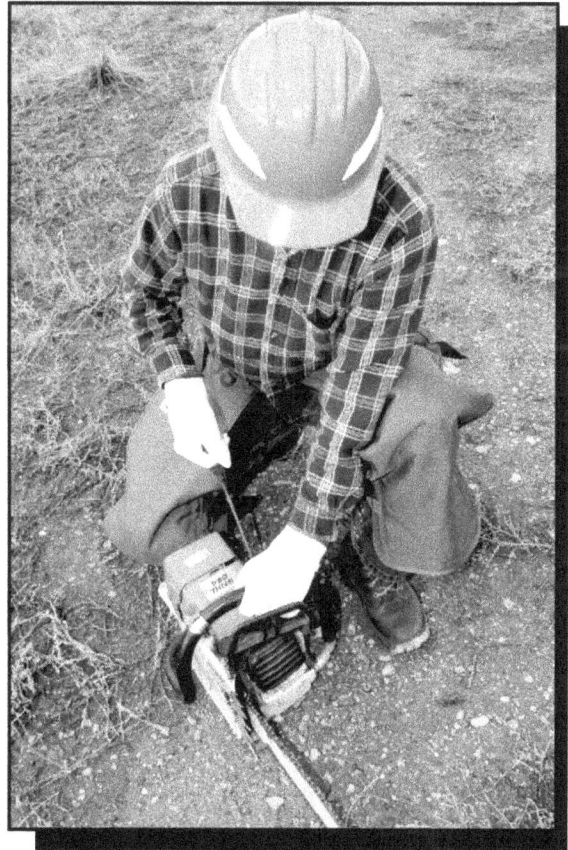

Figure 3-17—Start the saw on firm ground.

Operational Safety

A full-wrap handlebar allows cutting from both sides of the tree using the bottom of the bar, the part of the bar that can be used aggressively. In some situations the ability to cut wood rapidly is critically important for safety. Full-wrap handlebars are designed to be used by both the left and the right hand. The sawyer's thumb should always be wrapped completely around the handlebar, no matter how the saw is turned. The thumb and fingers are essential for maintaining control of the chain saw, especially during a kickback. The grip on the chain saw should be firm, but not overly tight.

Handling—

- Never operate a chain saw with one hand. You do not have control of the saw and increase the risk that you will be injured if the saw kicks back.
- Always grip the saw firmly with both hands.
- Grasp the throttle handle firmly with your dominant hand and grasp the handlebar with your less dominant hand. Your fingers must encircle the handlebar with the thumb wrapped underneath.
- Never operate a chain saw with the throttle lock engaged. If you do, you will not be able to control the saw or the chain speed.
- Make sure your work area is clear of people and obstacles, such as rocks, stumps, holes, or roots that may cause you to stumble or fall.
- Make sure that the saw chain does not contact any materials such as rocks or wire. Such contact is a safety hazard and will dull the chain. The chain will require filing or it may be damaged in ways that filing cannot correct.
- Cutting with the bottom of the bar pulls the chain saw away from the sawyer. Cutting with the top of the bar pushes the saw back at the sawyer. Cutting with the bottom of the bar increases efficiency and decreases the sawyer's fatigue.

Reactive Forces—The laws of physics explain that for every action there is an equal and opposite reaction. These reactions happen very quickly during chain saw operation and can be dangerous.

Kickback—Kickback is the most powerful reactive force you will encounter while operating a chain saw. Kickback can occur while felling, limbing, bucking, or brushing when the upper quadrant of the bar nose contacts a solid object or is pinched (figure 3-18).

During kickback, the bar is forced up and back in an uncontrolled arc toward the sawyer. Many factors determine the severity of the kickback and the arc, including: chain speed, angle of contact, condition of the chain, and the speed at which the bar contacts the object.

Ways to avoid kickback:
- Hold the saw with both hands, securely gripping the handle and the handlebar between your thumb and forefinger.
- Be aware of the location of the bar's nose at all times.
- Never let the bar's nose contact another object.
- Never cut with the power head higher than your shoulder.
- Never overreach.
- Pull the saw smoothly out of the cuts. This technique will help to reduce kickbacks and fatigue.
- Cut one log at a time.
- Stand to the side of the kickback arc.
- Use caution when entering a partially completed cut.
- Use a properly sharpened and tensioned chain at all times.
- Watch the cut and the log for any movement that may pinch the chain.
- Use a low kickback chain.

Figure 3-18—Kickback occurs when the upper quadrant of the bar nose contacts a solid object or is pinched.—Oregon Maintenance and Safety Manual, *permission by Blount, Inc.*

Pushback—Pushback (figure 3-19) occurs when the chain on the top of the bar is suddenly stopped by contacting another object or by being pinched. The chain drives the saw straight back toward the sawyer.

Figure 3-19—Pushback occurs when the chain on the top of the bar is suddenly stopped by contacting another object or by being pinched.—*From* Chain Safety Manual, *permission by Stihl, Inc.*

Ways to avoid pushback:

- Only cut with the top of the bar when necessary.
- Watch the cut and the log for any movement that may pinch the top of the bar.
- Do not twist the bar when removing it from a boring cut or underbuck.

Pull-In—Pull-in occurs when the chain on the bottom of the bar is caught or pinched, and suddenly stops. The chain pulls the saw forward (figure 3-20).

Figure 3-20—Pull-in occurs when the chain on the bottom of the bar is suddenly stopped by contacting another object or by being pinched.—*From* Chain Safety Manual, *permission by Stihl, Inc.*

Ways to avoid pull-in:
- Always start a cut with the chain at or near full speed and with the bumper spikes (dogs) contacting the wood.
- Watch the cut and the log for any movement that may pinch the bar. Use wedges to keep the cut open.

Additional Tools

This section includes information about axes, wedges, approved safety containers for fuel and oil, peaveys, and cant hooks.

Axes—Axes are used to remove bark from trees and to drive wedges during felling and bucking. The ax handle should be smooth and free of cracks. The head should be securely attached to the handle. Axes used for driving wedges should have a straight handle.

Single-bit axes need to be heavy enough (3 to 5 pounds) to drive plastic wedges into the trees being felled. The back of the ax (poll) should be smooth, have rounded edges, and be free of burrs to minimize damage to wedges. Pulaskis should never be used to drive wedges.

Always remove branches, underbrush, overhead obstructions, or debris that might interfere with limbing and chopping. Do not allow anyone to stand in the immediate area. Make sure workers know how far materials may fly. Protect all workers against flying chips and other chopping hazards by requiring them to wear the appropriate PPE.

Always position your body securely while working with a tool. Never chop crosshanded; always use a natural striking action. Be alert when working on hillsides or uneven ground. If you cut a sapling that is held down by a fallen log, the sapling may spring back. Be alert for sudden breakage. If you do not need to cut something, leave it alone.

Never use chopping tools as wedges or mauls. Do not allow two persons to chop or drive wedges together on the same tree. When chopping limbs from a felled tree, stand on the opposite side of the log from the limb being chopped and swing toward the top of the tree or branch. Do not allow the tool handle to drop below a plane that is parallel with the ground unless you are chopping on the side of a tree opposite your body.

If the cutting edge picks up a wood chip, stop. Remove the chip before continuing. To prevent blows from glancing, keep the striking angle of the tool head perpendicular to the tree trunk.

Wedges—Wedges are essential tools for safe felling and bucking. They provide a way to lift the tree, preventing the tree from sitting back when it is being felled. A wedge must be inserted into the back cut as soon as possible. Wedges also reduce binds on the saw when bucking logs.

Select the correct wedge for the job. The proper type, size, and length or a wedge varies, depending on its use. The size of the tree being felled or the material being bucked determines the size of the wedge that will be needed. If the wedge is too small, it may be ineffective. If the wedge is too long, it may not be able to do its job without being driven so far into the tree that it contacts the chain.

Always drive wedges by striking them squarely on the head. Drive them carefully to prevent them from flying out of the cut.

Check wedges daily or before each job. Do not use cracked or flawed wedges. Wedges that are damaged need to be cleaned up before they are used again.

Grind wedges to the manufacturer's original shape and angle. Wear eye protection and a dust mask.

Repair any driving tool or remove it from service when its head begins to chip or mushroom.

Carry wedges in an appropriate belt or other container, not in the pockets of clothing.

Most wedges are made out of plastic or soft metal, such as magnesium, and come in different sizes. Use plastic wedges in both felling and bucking operations to prevent the saw chain from being damaged if it contacts the wedges.

The two basic types of wedges used in sawing are single and double taper.

Single-taper wedges (figure 3-21) are simple inclined planes designed to provide lift during tree felling. As the wedge is driven into the back cut, the tree hinges on the holding wood, redistributing the tree's weight. The sawyer must coordinate striking the wedge with the forward sway of the tree, allowing the wedge to be driven more easily and sending less of a shock wave up the tree. Striking the wedge when the tree is in its backward sway sends a severe shock wave up the tree and can knock out dead branches or tops, endangering the sawyer. Sawyers should look up for falling material after each blow to the wedge.

Figure 3-21—A rifled single-taper wedge is designed to provide lift during tree felling. It can be stacked with additional rifled single-taper wedges.

Double-taper wedges (figure 3-22) are designed to reduce bind. They taper equally on both sides from the centerline, forcing the wood to move equally in both directions. They perform best when used in bucking to prevent the kerf from closing, which would cause the guide bar to bind.

Figure 3-22—Double-taper wedges are designed to reduce bind.

Fuel and Oil Containers—Use Forest Service-approved containers to transport fuel and oil. All lids shall be fully sealed prior to transport.

• Even empty containers are dangerous.
• If a container is missing a lid or showing signs of a defect such as cracks, take it out of service immediately.
• All employees who handle, transport, or use flammable or combustible liquids shall receive hazard communication standards training and be familiar with material safety data sheets.
• Passengers shall not ride in the enclosed cargo portion of a vehicle hauling flammable or combustible liquids. If it is absolutely necessary to carry flammable or combustible liquids with a passenger vehicle, a minimum amount of such cargo shall be secured in a rack on the roof.
• Never transport fuel in the same cargo area with oxidizers, acids, or radio equipment.
• Flammable or combustible liquids shall be carried in Forest Service-approved containers. Such containers shall be clearly labeled to identify the contents.

Containers shall never be filled more than 90 percent with fuel. Fuel vapors need room to expand. A chain saw should be fueled only after the saw has cooled completely.

Fueling a Chain Saw—

• Allow the saw to cool for at least 5 minutes before refueling.

• Fill the saw on bare ground or other noncombustible surface.

• Immediately clean up spilled fuel.

• Refuel outdoors and at least 20 feet from any open flame or other sources of ignition.

• Do not start the saw closer than 10 feet from the fueling area.

Peaveys and Cant Hooks—The blacksmith Joseph Peavey invented the peavey (figure 3-23a). Both the peavey and the cant hook (figure 3-23b) use a curved metal hook on the end of a straight handle to roll or skid logs. A peavey has a sharp pointed spike at the lower end, while a cant hook has a tow or lip. Most peaveys and cant hooks come with a duckbill hook that is a good all-around style. Peaveys and cant hooks come with hickory handles that are from 2 to 5½ feet long.

Figure 3-23b—The cant hook has a tow or lip at the lower end instead of a pointed spike like the peavey.

Figure 3-23a—Peaveys are used in the woods to pry logs.

Peaveys are used almost exclusively in the woods. Peaveys are handy for prying logs up onto blocks to keep the saw from pinching while bucking. The cant hook is used primarily to roll logs.

• Keep the handle free of splinters, splits, and cracks.

• Keep the point sharp.

• Keep your body balanced when pushing or pulling the pole.

• Grip the handle firmly. Do not overstress it.

• Carry the peavey with the point forward, grasping it just behind the point of attachment of the hook. Secure the hook to the shaft to prevent it from swinging free.

• Place a guard on the point when the tool is not in use.

Chapter 4—Chain Saw Tasks and Techniques (Suggested time: 2 hours)

Chapter Objectives:

- Students will learn the importance of a thorough sizeup before limbing, brushing, slashing, bucking, and felling operations.
- Students will understand the skills needed to operate a chain saw safely and efficiently.
- Students will understand the types of binds.
- Students will learn the procedures for limbing, bucking, and felling.

Limbing

Any of the following situations could result in a fatality or serious injury.

Check for overhead hazards before any limbing begins. If a specific portion of the tree you are limbing has any overhead hazards, leave that portion of the tree unlimbed.

Check for objects on the ground such as stumps, logs, and spring poles that may be hidden by the limbs of the felled tree. If the tip of the bar unintentionally strikes an object, the saw may kick back.

Maintain a firm grip on the saw with your thumb wrapped around the handlebar during all limbing activities, regardless of the direction the saw is turned.

Be sure you have firm footing as you walk down the tree that you are limbing. Calked boots are strongly recommended for walking on felled trees.

Do not attempt to cut limbs that are supporting a tree off the ground if there's a chance the tree could roll on the sawyer. Always plan and clear an escape route.

When limbing on top of a log, right-handed sawyers should limb the right side out to the top before turning around and limbing the other side on their way back. Another option is to limb a tree out in sections. It is not advisable for a right-handed sawyer to limb on the left side (or for a left-handed sawyer to limb on the right side). Crossing over when limbing could result in an injury.

- The bar length should be appropriate for the sawyer's height. Proper bar length reduces bending at the waist, decreasing back strain.
- To increase the distance between the saw chain and your leg, bend at the waist and reach out with the saw to cut the limb. This increased distance allows you more reaction time if a kickback occurs.

Overreaching kickbacks occur when too much bar is used when cutting a limb and the bar tip contacts an object, propelling the bar up and back (figure 4-1).

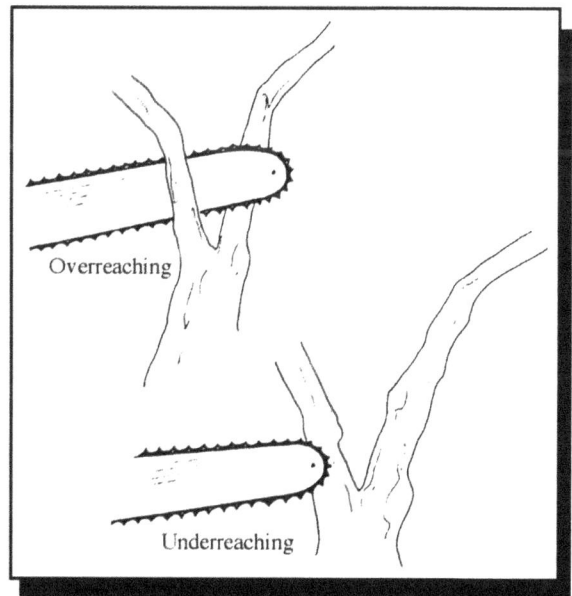

Figure 4-1—Avoid overreaching and underreaching kickbacks by using the bar properly.

Underreaching kickbacks occur when too little of the bar tip is used and the tip contacts any object, propelling the bar back and down.

Spring poles are generally small-diameter trees or brush that are pinned under larger trees. Because the small-diameter trees or brush are still rooted, they are under tension when they become pinned. If this tension is undetected, the spring poles can spring back with tremendous force when they are cut, striking the sawyer or throwing the chain saw back into the sawyer. Cut a spring pole only when necessary.

- To remove spring poles properly, begin by relieving some of the tension in a controlled manner. Stand back a safe distance and make a series of shallow cuts about ½ inch apart on the underside of the spring pole. Be careful not to cut too deep. During each cut, as soon as you detect movement, remove the saw and begin the next cut. Four to six cuts on the underside of the spring pole should be sufficient.
- The release cut is made from the top, about one-half inch past the end of the series of cuts on the underside and on the piece that is going to fall to the ground. Be sure you are clear of the piece that will be released.

Sometimes a tree is suspended off the ground by the limbs underneath or by uneven terrain. The sawyer must decide whether or not to limb the tree after considering the potential that the sawyer might fall or that the tree might roll or collapse. Consider the choice of footwear and environmental conditions, such as rain, snow, fog, or darkness, and the ability and experience of the sawyer. Carefully select the appropriate technique, such as limbing from the ground, limbing on top, or lowering the tree by bucking (figure 4-2).

Figure 4-2—The top side of suspended logs should be limbed while you are standing on the ground or you can buck the log to lower it to the ground before limbing.

Brushing and Slashing

Sizeup and Safety Considerations

Engage the chain brake when moving short distances and be sure the chain has stopped before moving to the next tree. Many sawyers have cut their chaps or their legs because the chain was moving when they took a step toward the next tree.

Shut the saw off when moving farther than from tree to tree, when hazardous conditions exist (slippery surfaces or heavy underbrush), and whenever moving more than 50 feet.

When slashing (felling) trees smaller than 5 inches in diameter, an undercut may not be needed. Instead, a single horizontal cut (kerf face) one-third the diameter of the tree may be used. When directional felling is necessary, use a normal face cut (consisting of a horizontal and sloping cut or two sloping cuts). Situations when directional felling should be used include:

- A potential barber-chair situation
- A closed canopy
- Tree defects
- Side binds
- Anticipated environmental damage

Other Mitigating Circumstances—Always escape the stump quickly, even when felling small-diameter trees. They can cause serious injuries and fatalities.

Trees should be pushed over only by the sawyer, only when the sawyer can do so safely, and only after the sawyer has looked up for overhead debris that could become dislodged.

Safe and Efficient Brushing and Slashing Techniques

In dense fuel accumulations, the tip of the guide bar may accidentally bump (stub) a limb. The sawyer must be alert continually for kickback.

Normally, the sawyer will have a hand piler working nearby helping to remove cut debris. The piler's safety must be taken into consideration.

Proper stance and saw handling is imperative. In addition, the following steps should be taken.

- *LOOK UP* for widow makers and other loose debris. Don't cut under a hazard. Remove the hazard or move the cutting location.
- When possible, stay on top of logs while limbing. Doing so reduces the chance that the log will roll over on the sawyer if the sawyer cuts a supporting limb.
- Watch out for whipping limbs and branches when cutting smaller material. Cut close to the stem. Begin and complete cuts with a sharp chain and high chain speed. Use eye protection.

- Cut limbs and stems flush with the trunk or close to the ground. Do not leave pointed stems that could cause injury during a fall or cause the sawyer to trip.
- Keep some distance between your legs and the guide bar. Bend down to maintain distance. Cut on one side, then the other to avoid moving the guide bar in front of you.
- Never cut with the chain saw above shoulder height (figure 4-3). Control is difficult when the saw's weight is above your shoulders. In addition, a thrown chain could strike you in the face or upper body.

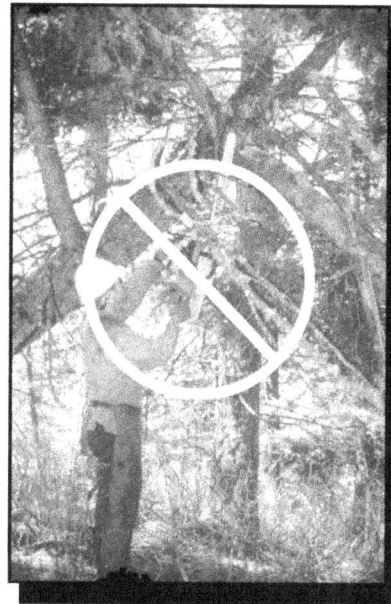

Figure 4-3—**DO NOT** cut with the chain saw above shoulder height. Keep the chain saw below your shoulders to maintain control when cutting.

- Clear debris from the cutting location to prevent the tip of the guide bar from stubbing it accidentally. When you are removing debris, engage the chain brake or turn off the ignition.
- Watch out for spring poles. Do not cut spring poles if you can avoid doing so. If you must cut a spring pole, make your release cut in the top side of the portion of the spring pole that will fall to the ground. Be careful not to stand in the path of the pole when tension is released.

• When cutting a heavy limb, consider using a small cut opposite the final cut to prevent the material from slabbing or peeling off.

• Pay special attention if you are working in close quarters with other workers in an area with steep slopes and thick brush or logging slash. First, stop and size up the situation. Make a plan and talk it over with all workers in the area. A well thought-out plan saves time and reduces the risk of accidents. After you've discussed the plan, work systematically from the outside in and from downhill up. This reduces the chance that material will hang up. Maintain a space between workers that is at least two-and-one-half times the height of the tallest tree.

You need one or more escape routes, even when slashing (felling) small trees. Begin to develop a pattern as you work into the area. As you down more material, be increasingly careful of your footing and continually identify new escape routes.

Special hazards like leaners and snags need to be taken care of right away. Get hazard trees on the ground so no one has to work under them (figure 4-4).

Double stumps (figure 4-5) are hazardous because they have a high potential for causing kickback. *Watch that bar tip!*

When slashing (felling) small trees, cut the stumps as close to the ground as possible without hitting the dirt with your chain. Stumps are cut low so they will not be as noticeable and will present fewer hazards for people and wildlife.

Small trees can be limbed while they are standing. Don't cut with the chain saw above shoulder height. Limbing the bottom of small trees allows the sawyer to move in closer to the bole when felling trees and will help the sawyer watch the tip of the bar to prevent kickbacks.

Figure 4-4—Hazard trees, such as leaners, need to be removed to prevent anyone from working under them.

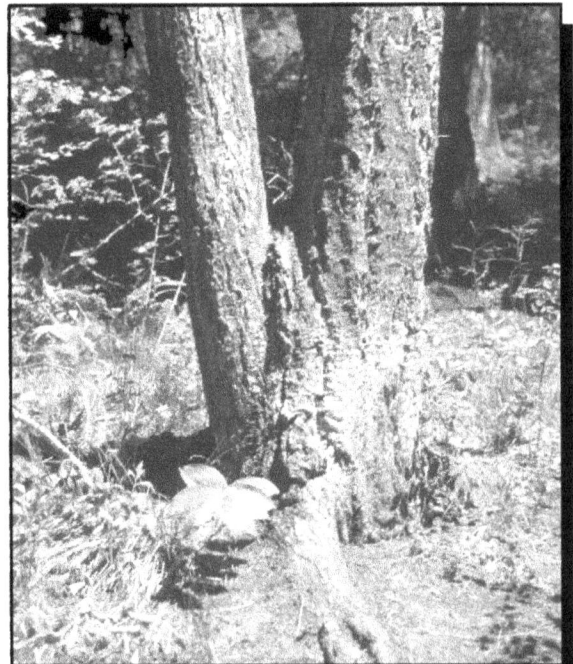

Figure 4-5—Double stumps have a high potential to cause kickback.

The chain is more likely to be thrown when you are working with small material. Check your chain tension often. Sawing close to the ground increases the chances of kickback and damage to the chain. Watch out for rocks and other debris.

Remember, when you saw up from the bottom (using the top of the bar) the saw will push back rather than pull away. This increases the risk of kickback and loss of control. Be aware of signs of fatigue like more frequent kickbacks, bar pinches, and near misses. Take a break when you show signs of fatigue.

Cut pieces small enough so they are easy to lift and handle. Lift properly using the legs and keeping the back straight. Hand pilers must be aware of their footing and watch out for flying debris.

Bucking

Situational Awareness

- Never buck a tree that exceeds your ability.
- Consider overhead hazards.
- Is the guide bar long enough for the tree that is being bucked?
- Establish good footing.
- Swamp out bucking areas and escape routes.
- Anticipate what will happen when the log is cut.
- Plan the bucking cut carefully after considering:
  - *Slope.* People and property in the cutting zone can be in the path of rolling logs.
  - *Tension.* Spring poles are trees under tension.
  - *Compression.* Falling or rolling root wads are unpredictable when compression is released.
  - *Rocks and foreign objects under the log.* The log will have a tendency to roll, slide, or bind. Broken

off limbs hidden underneath the log can roll up and strike the sawyer.

The Forest Service *Health and Safety Code Handbook* emphasizes the following points:

- Assess the area for overhead hazards before beginning bucking.
- Size up the log for possible reaction after the release cut has been completed.
- Establish escape routes and clear any obstacles that might inhibit your escape.
- Cut slowly and observe the kerf for movement that will indicate the location of a bind. A log can have different types of binds at different places.

Safe and Efficient Bucking Techniques

In most situations it is safest to buck logs from the uphill side unless the log may move uphill when it is bucked. This could occur because of the log's position, weight distribution, and pivot points. Always consider binds and pivot points. Consult another sawyer if you have questions.

Learn to use the saw's bumper spikes (dogs) as a pivot point when you are felling or bucking. This technique will enhance your control of the saw and improve the saw's efficiency, while reducing fatigue.

Begin bucking by cutting the offside first. This is the side the log might move to when it is cut, normally the downhill side. Cut straight down until you have space for a wedge.

- Always protect the saw chain from becoming dull. This will reduce fatigue and lessen chances of kickbacks and barber chairs. (Barber chairs will be addressed later.)
- Keep the chain out of the dirt and rocks.
- When cutting uprooted trees with dirt and rocks in

the bark, use an ax to trim the bark away from the area to be cut.

Insert a wedge or wedges to prevent the cut (kerf) from closing tightly and pinching the bar.

Understanding directional pressures—or binds—is important for safe and efficient cutting. These binds determine bucking techniques and procedures. Look for landforms, stumps, blowdown, and other obstacles that prevent a log from lying flat, causing binds. When a bind occurs, different pressure areas result (figure 4-6). The tension area is the portion of the log where the wood fibers are being stretched apart. In this portion of the log, the chain saw's cut (kerf) opens as the cut is made. The other pressure area is called the compression area. Here the wood fibers push together. In this portion of the log, the kerf closes as the cut is made. It is extremely important to determine what will happen to the log when it is cut. Inspect the log for all binds, pivot points, and natural skids. Various bucking techniques can be used to lower a suspended tree to the ground.

Figure 4-6—The log is being pulled apart by tension force and pushed together by compression force. Areas of tension and compression occur on opposite sides of the log.

Determining Bind—The four types of bind are: top, bottom, side, and end. Normally, logs have a combination of two or more binds (figure 4-7).

Top bind—The tension area is on the bottom of the log. The compression area is on the top.
Bottom bind—The tension area is on the top of the log. The compression area is on the bottom.

Side bind—Pressure is exerted sideways on the log.
End bind—Weight compresses the log's entire cross section.

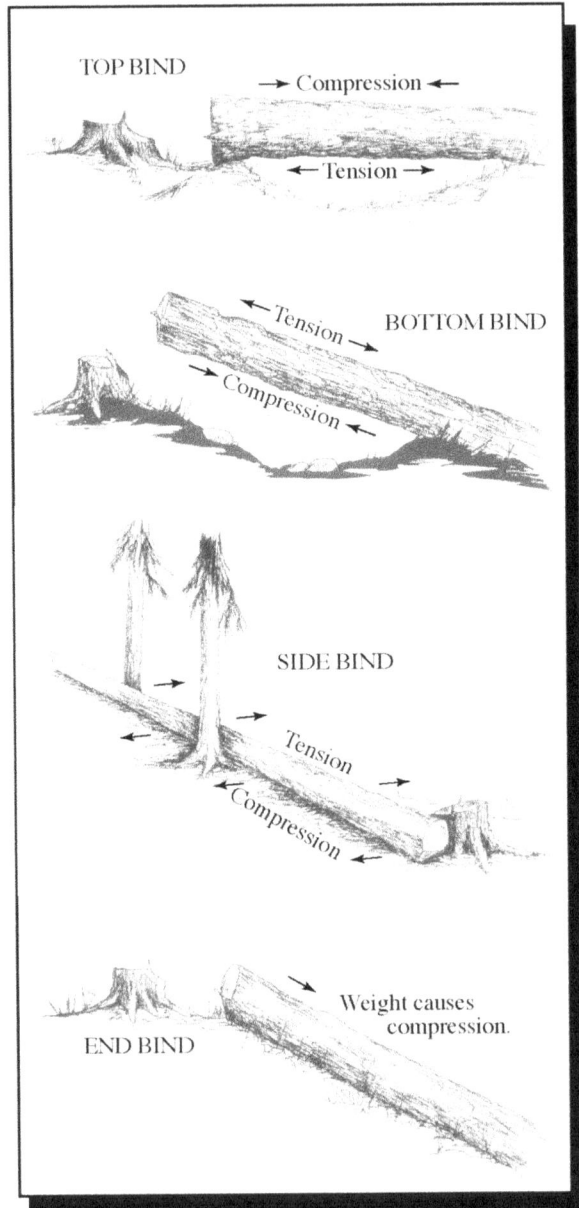

Figure 4-7-There are four types of binds. A log can have a combination of two or more binds.

42

It is best to start bucking at the small end of the log and work toward the butt end, removing the binds in the smaller material first. Look for broken limbs and tops above the working area. Never stand under an overhead hazard while bucking.

Look for small trees and limbs (spring poles) bent under the log being bucked. They may spring up as the log rolls away. If you can safely do so, cut these hazards before the log is bucked (figure 4-8). Otherwise, move to a new cutting location and flag the hazard.

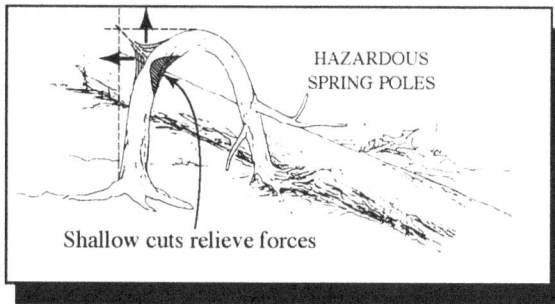

Figure 4-8—Look out for spring poles (trees or limbs that are being held down by other trees.) Spring poles can release with great force, causing serious injuries. Make a series of shallow cuts on the inside of the bend when severing a spring pole.

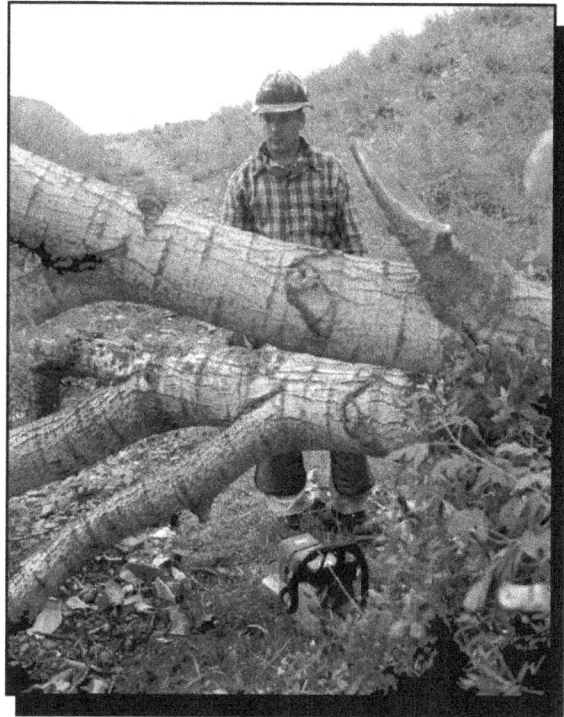

Figure 4-9—Determine the offside. It is the side the log might move to when it is cut.

Determine the offside. It is the side the log might move to when it is cut—normally the downhill side (figure 4-9). Watch out for possible pivots. Clear the work area and escape paths. Allow more than 8 feet of room to escape when the final cut is made. Establish solid footing and remove debris that may hinder your escape.

Determine the cutting sequence before beginning to cut (figure 4-10). Cut the offside first from a safe position. If possible, make a cut about one-third the diameter of log. This allows the sawyer to step back from the log on the final cut. Do not let the tip of the bar hit any object.

Watch the kerf to detect log movement. Position yourself so you can detect a slight opening or closing of the kerf: there is no better indicator of the log's reaction on the

Figure 4-10—Determine the cutting sequence before beginning to cut.

release cut. If the bind cannot be determined, proceed with caution. It may be necessary to move the saw back and forth slowly in the kerf (about 3 seconds for each chain revolution) to prevent the saw from getting bound as the kerf closes behind the guide bar. Cut only deep enough to place a wedge. Continue cutting. Watch the kerf (figure 4-11). If the kerf starts to open, there is a bottom bind; if the kerf starts to close, there is a top bind.

Visually project the kerf's location to the bottom of the log. Reduce the amount of wood for the final cut by cutting a short distance into the log along this line. Be prepared for kickback.

Figure 4-11—Watch the kerf for movement that will indicate a bottom bind (kerf opens) or top bind (kerf closes).

The sequence of the remaining cuts depends on the type of bind. Generally the next cut will be a small (less than 1½ inches) pie-shaped cut removed from the compression area. The log can settle slowly into this space, preventing dangerous slabbing and splintering. This practice is extremely important when cutting large logs.

The final cut, or release cut, will be made through the tension area. Because the offside has been cut, the sawyer only has to use enough bar to finish cutting the remaining wood. This allows the sawyer to stand back, away from the danger. The location of the pie-shaped section and the release cut vary depending on the type of bind.

Top Bind: Remove the pie-shaped section from the top and make the release cut from the bottom.

Bottom Bind: Remove the pie-shaped section from the bottom and make the release cut from the top.

Side Bind: If you are not certain the job is safe, do not make the cut. Normally, the offside is the side with tension; the tension side is usually bowed out (convex). Look for solid trees with no overhead hazards or other objects that you can stand behind for protection while cutting. Remove a pie-shaped section from the compression area, and then make the release cut in the tension area.

End Bind: Cut from the top down, inserting a wedge as soon as possible. Finish by cutting down from the top. Watch the wood chips to make sure that the chain is not cutting in the dirt (look for dark chips).

Safe Bucking Practices

Buck small sections that will be easy to control when they begin moving. Removing a single section of log may require that other binds be eliminated first. Angled bucking cuts, wide on top and made on the offside, allow a single section of log to be rolled away from the remaining log.

All logs must be completely severed when bucked. Flagging should be used to mark an incompletely bucked log as a hazard.

Pay special attention when bucking in blowdown. Blowdown is a result of strong winds that have uprooted the trees. At any time while the bucking cuts are made, the roots can drop back into place or roll. Consider the following points when bucking blowdown:

- Small trees growing on the roots of blowdown could be forced into the sawyer's position if the roots drop or roll. Cut the small trees first. Limbs may be preventing the roots from rolling. Don't cut those limbs.
- The roots can move in any direction. Avoid standing directly behind or downhill from them.

The following example shows the importance of following proper procedures when bucking blowdown.

A 30-inch d.b.h. fir tree was lying across a steep slope; the butt end was still anchored by a few roots. About 30 feet from the roots, the tree was balanced on a small stump. This stump supported the small end of the tree above some log chunks and debris.

The first step in proper bucking procedure is to inspect the log for all binds, pivot points, and skids. The sawyer failed to properly estimate the log's reaction when the log was cut. He chose downhill as his offside, expecting both the tree and roots to roll down the slope. He stood 12 feet from the roots and to the left of his saw.

Warn workers who are working in or below an active cutting area. Allow workers time to move to a safe location. Verify their safety visually and verbally. Announce when a bucking operation has been completed.

Never approach a cutting operation from below until the saw has stopped running, you have established communication with the sawyer, and the sawyer has granted permission to proceed.

Points to Remember—
- Do a complete sizeup. Identify the hazards, and establish your escape routes and safety zones.
- Use objects such as rocks, stumps (if they are tall enough), and sound, standing trees with no overhead hazards for protection in the event the tree springs sideways toward the sawyer when the release cut is made.
- Binds change with log movement; reevaluate as necessary.
- When possible, remove compression before tension.

When the sawyer made his release cut, the log rolled slightly uphill, off the small stump. The tree's top came to rest on the log chunks and debris, and then slid rapidly downhill on these natural skids. With the stump as a pivot, the butt end swung uphill, killing the sawyer.

If the small log had been inspected thoroughly, the sawyer could have:

- Bucked the tree at or near the pivot.
- Started bucking at the small end of the tree first, leaving the roots for last.
- Stood to the right of his saw, so he would be in the clear.

Basic Felling

Situational Awareness

Analyze the felling job by considering:

- Species (live or dead)
- Size and length
- Soundness or defects
- Twin tops
- Widow makers and hangups
- Spike top
- Rusty (discolored) knots
- Punky (swollen and sunken) knots
- Frozen wood
- Footing
- Heavy snow loading
- Bark soundness
- Direction of lean
- Degree of lean (slight or great)
- Head lean or side lean
- Nesting or feeding holes
- Splits and frost cracks
- Deformities, such as those caused by mistletoe
- Heavy branches or uneven weight distribution
- Damage by lightning or fire

Check the base of the tree for:

- Thud (hollow) sound when struck
- Conks and mushrooms
- Shelf or bracket fungi
- Wounds or scars
- Split trunk
- Insect activity
- Feeding holes
- Bark soundness
- Resin flow on bark
- Unstable root system or root protrusions

Examine surrounding terrain for:

- Steepness
- Irregularities in the ground
- Draws and ridges
- Rocks
- Stumps
- Loose logs
- Ground debris that can fly or kick up at the sawyer

Examine the immediate work area for:

- People, roads, or vehicles
- Powerlines
- Hangups and widow makers
- Snags
- Fire-weakened trees
- Reserve trees
- Structures
- Openings to fall trees into
- Other trees that may be affected
- Hazards such as trees, rocks, brush, or low-hanging limbs
- Other trees that may have to be felled first

Sizeup

Before starting the saw, the chain saw operator must be able to evaluate if a tree is safe to cut. Other options are always available. *If felling a particular tree is dangerous, don't do it!*

Walk out and thoroughly check the intended lay or bed where the tree is supposed to fall. Look for dead treetops, snags, and widow makers that may cause kickbacks, allow the tree to roll, or result in another tree or limb becoming a hazard.

The escape route and alternate routes must be predetermined paths where the sawyer can escape once the tree is committed to fall or has been bucked. Sawyers must select and prepare the work area and clear escape routes and alternate routes before starting the first cut. Escape routes and safe zones should be 90 to 135 degrees from the direction of fall. Safe zones should be no less than 20 feet from the stump, preferably behind another tree that is sound and large enough to provide protection.

Observe the Top—When you approach the tree to be felled, observe the top. Debris falling from above causes most accidents. Check for all overhead hazards that may come down during felling.

Look at the limbs. Are they heavy enough on one side to affect the desired felling direction? Do the limbs have heavy accumulations of ice and snow?

Are the limbs entangled with the limbs of other trees? If so, they will snap off or prevent the tree from falling after it has been cut.

Is the wind blowing strong enough to affect the tree's fall? Windspeeds higher than 15 miles per hour may require that felling be stopped. Strong winds also could blow over other trees and snags in the area. Shifting or erratic winds require special safety considerations.

Check For Snags—Check all snags in the immediate area for soundness. A gust of wind may cause snags to fall at any time, as may the vibration of a tree fall. If it is safe to do so, begin by removing any snag in the cutting area that poses a threat.

Swamp Out the Base—Clear small trees, brush, and debris from the base of the tree. Remove all material that could cause you to trip or lose your balance. Also remove material that will interfere with the saw, wedges, and ax. Look for small trees and brush that could accidentally stub the guide bar. Be careful not to fatigue yourself with unnecessary swamping. Remove only what is needed to work safely around the base of the tree.

Assess the Tree's Lean and the Soundness of the Holding Wood—Most trees have two natural leans; the predominant head lean and the secondary side lean. The leaning weight of the tree will be a combination of these two leans. Both must be considered when determining the desired felling direction.

The desired felling direction usually can be chosen within 45 degrees of the combined lean, provided there is enough sound holding (hinge) wood to work with, especially in the corners of the undercut.

Evaluate the tree's lean. Using a weight as a plumb bob or an ax, project a vertical line up from the center of the tree's butt and determine if the tree's top lies to the right or left of the projected line (figure 4-12).

Figure 4-12—Assess the tree for head lean and side lean.

A pistol-grip tree may appear to be leaning in one direction while most of the weight is actually leaning in another direction (figure 4-13). Look at the treetop from at least two different spots at right angles to each other.

Figure 4-13—The lean of a pistol-grip tree is hard to determine.

TOP
VIEW

Figure 4-14—Do not weaken the holding wood by boring into or across any of the holding wood.

The importance of the holding wood cannot be overemphasized. Determine the condition of the holding wood by sounding it with an ax. Look up for falling debris while doing so.

Boring is an important technique. The color of the sawdust and the ease with which the saw enters the wood will be your indications of the tree's soundness. Boring must be done properly because it has the potential for kickback. Using the guide bar's tip, bore vertically at 90 degrees to the holding wood (figure 4-14). Begin the boring cut with the chain saw lower than the tip of the bar. After the tip is deep enough in the tree to prevent it from kicking back, apply full throttle. Your thumb should be wrapped securely around the top of the handlebar. Maintain full throttle throughout the boring cut.

Check for frost cracks or other weak areas in the holding wood. The desired felling direction can be adjusted to eliminate weaknesses in the holding wood. The depth of the undercut also can be adjusted (less than one-third the tree's diameter or greater than one-third) so that the holding area takes advantage of the soundest wood available.

Escape Routes and Safety Zones

With the desired felling direction in mind, determine your escape routes and safety zones (figure 4-15). Consider the side of the tree where you will make your final cut. Don't choose a path directly behind the tree. Escape routes and safety zones should be 90 to 135 degrees from the direction of fall. It is best to prepare two escape routes in case you switch your location on the final cut.

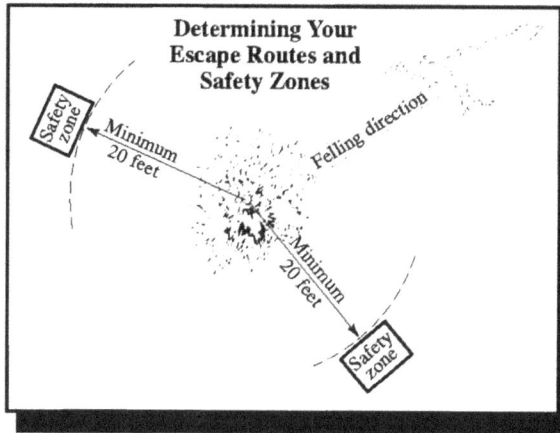

Figure 4-15—Keep the felling direction in mind when planning escape routes.

Look for a large solid tree or rock for protection. Safety zones must be at least 20 feet away from the stump and not be directly behind it. Make sure that debris that could trip you is cleared from the escape routes. Practice the escape.

Walk out the intended lay of the tree (figure 4-16). Look for any obstacles that could cause the tree to kick back over the stump or cause the butt to jump or pivot as the tree hits the ground. Look for any small trees or snags that could be thrown into your escape routes. Check to be sure the cutting area is clear of people.

Figure 4-16—Check the intended lay of the tree for obstacles.

Using the observations you made walking out the lay, reexamine the escape routes. Be sure that your chosen routes will be the safest escapes—before you begin to cut.

Beginning the Cut

Assume a comfortable stance for sawing, either standing upright or on one knee. If there is any danger from above, such as snags, the cutting should be done while standing so the sawyer can watch the top and escape more quickly.

The undercut (or face cut) is made in the direction you want the tree to fall. Estimate one-third of the tree's diameter, set the saw's bumper spikes to cut that far, shout a warning if necessary, and proceed with the undercut. When finished, check the direction the tree is faced (figure 4-17). If the face is not in the desired felling direction, correct the cut.

Figure 4-17—Check the direction the tree is faced.

Reexamine your primary and secondary escape routes before beginning the back cut. Shut off the saw and make sure that the cutting area is secure. Shout a warning (figure 4-18).

49

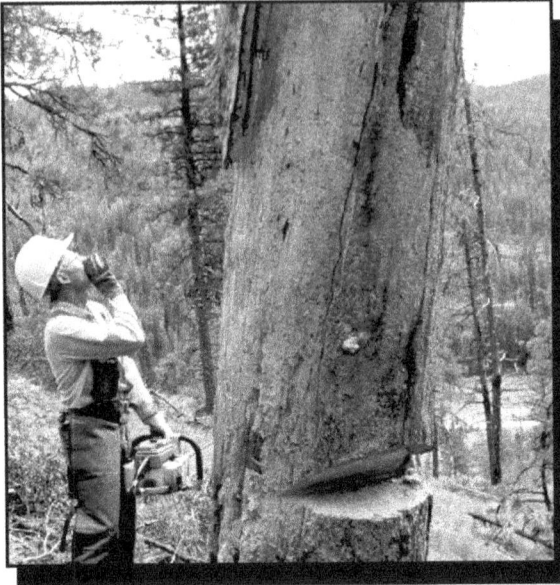

Figure 4-18—Shout a warning to make sure the cutting area is secure.

Remember the importance of holding wood, stump shot (see glossary), and wedging, then complete the back cut (figure 4-19).

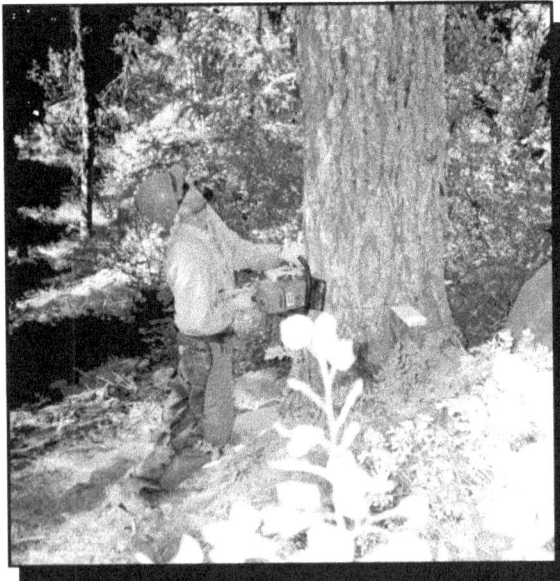

Figure 4-19—Complete the back cut.

Escape. When the tree commits to the fall, leave rapidly, following your escape route. Do not hesitate at the stump. If your saw becomes stuck, leave it. If carrying the saw prevents you from escaping quickly enough, **_drop it!_**

Keep your eyes on your predetermined escape route. If the felled tree strikes other trees, they may still be moving after the tree has fallen. Watch for flying limbs and tops. Remain in your safety zone until it is safe to approach the stump.

Analyze the operation. The stump gives the best critique of the felling operation (figure 4-20). Before approaching the stump, look in the tops of the surrounding trees for new overhead hazards.

Figure 4-20—Look at the stump when critiquing a felling operation.

Take a moment or two to look at the stump. Did the tree fall where it was intended? How much holding wood is left on each corner? Is the stump shot sufficient? Were the cuts level? Take time to analyze the felling operation. Check the stump height and look for stump or root pull and dutchman cuts.

Felling the Tree

Proper evaluation of a felling operation requires a thorough understanding of the mechanics of the undercut, holding wood, back cut, and the felling procedure. In addition, the sawyer needs to consider the various tree problems. Every tree should be evaluated (sized up) using techniques discussed in *Situational Awareness* in chapter 2.

The Undercut, Holding Wood, and Back Cut—The three basic cuts are the conventional undercut, the Humboldt, and the open face. We are only going to discuss the conventional undercut because of its broad application for all timber types, and because it provides a solid foundation from which to learn additional cutting techniques.

It takes three cuts to fell a tree. Two cuts form the undercut (or face cut) and the third forms the back cut (figure 4-21). The correct relationship of these cuts results in safe and effective tree felling. Before discussing the felling procedure, we will analyze the mechanics of the felling cuts. Undercutting and back cutting construct the hinge that controls the direction and fall of the tree.

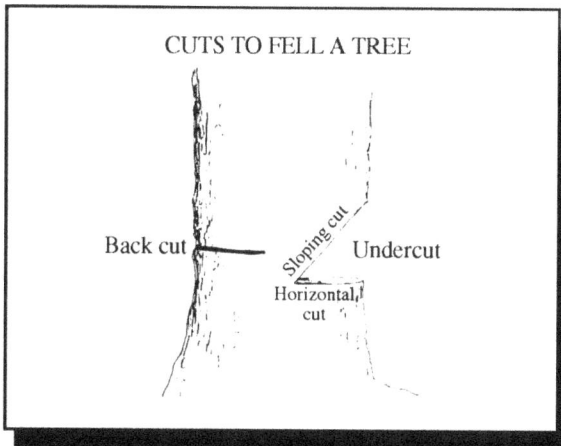

CUTS TO FELL A TREE

Back cut   Sloping cut   Undercut

Horizontal cut

Figure 4-21—A horizontal cut and a sloping cut make up the undercut. The back cut is the third cut needed to fell a tree.

The undercut serves two purposes. First, it allows the tree to fall in the chosen direction by removing the tree's support in the direction of the face. Second, it enables control because the tree slips off the stump, rather than jumping off.

The undercut consists of two cuts, a horizontal cut and a sloping cut. Observe overhead hazards and look up often during the undercut.

The horizontal cut is a level cut. This cut is made close to the ground unless a snag is being felled or another factor creates special hazards for the sawyer. The horizontal cut dictates the direction of fall if the relationships of the three cuts are maintained. After selecting the desired felling direction, estimate one-third the tree's diameter, set the saw's bumper spikes to cut that far, and begin the horizontal cut.

The specific direction of the undercut is determined by "gunning" the saw. Look down the gunning marks on the saw and align them with the desired felling direction. After the cut has been made level to at least one-third of the tree's diameter, the horizontal cut is complete. Trees with heavy leans may not allow the sawyer to make the horizontal cut as deep as one-third of the tree's diameter without pinching the guide bar.

Ideally, the undercut is made in the same direction as the tree's lean, but because of structures, roads, other trees, or trails, the desired felling direction may be to one side or the other of the lean. Normally, the desired direction is less than 45 degrees from the lean.

When the horizontal cut is complete, remove the bark from an area on both sides of the kerf. The bark can be removed with your ax or with the tip of the guide bar (figure 4-22). Watch out in case the ax glances off the bole or the saw kicks back.

Figure 4-22—Bark can be removed with the tip of the bar.

Figure 4-23—The sloping cut is a 45-degree angle.

Figure 4-24—When the sloping cut and the horizontal cut do not meet exactly, a dutchman is formed. This kerf-wide cut makes the direction of the tree's fall harder to predict. It can also cause the tree to barber chair, lifting the log off the stump and placing the sawyer at great risk.

The sloping cut needs to be angled so that when the face closes the tree is fully committed to the planned direction of fall. As the face closes, the holding wood breaks. If this happens and the tree is still standing straight, the tree could fall away from the desired direction.

As a general rule, make the sloping cut at a 45-degree angle (figure 4-23). Remember that it is important that the face not close until the tree is fully committed to the planned direction of fall.

Line up the sloping cut with the horizontal cut so that they meet, but do not cross. When the cuts cross, a dutchman (figure 4-24) is formed. If the tree were felled with a dutchman, first the dutchman would close, then the tree would split vertically (barber chair), or the holding wood would break off. Felling control would be lost. A weak tree might snap off somewhere along the bole or at the top. It is difficult to make the sloping cut and the horizontal cut meet correctly on the opposite side of the tree. This is because the point of intersection is not immediately visible to the sawyer.

After making a short sloping cut, leave the saw in the cut. Go around to the other side of the tree and see if the guide bar is in the correct plane to intersect the back of the horizontal cut. Keep your finger away from the throttle trigger while engaging the chain brake.

Practicing on high stumps will help you become skilled at lining up these cuts.

The holding wood is the wood immediately behind the undercut. The most important portion of the holding wood is in the very corners of the cut, in the first 4 to 8 inches inside the bark. The horizontal and sloping cuts must not overlap in this region. If they do, the undercut must be cleaned up so no dutchman is left in these corners. Care must be taken not to cut the undercut too deeply while cleaning up. This will reduce the amount of room available for wedges during the back cut.

If cleaning up the sloping cut will create too deep of an undercut, stop the sloping cut directly above the end of the horizontal cut.

The undercut needs to be cleaned out. Any remaining wood will cause the cut to close prematurely and the holding wood will be broken behind the closure.

Once the undercut has been cleaned, recheck the felling direction. Place the saw in the undercut and check the gunning marks (figure 4-25) or stick an ax head into the undercut and look down the length of the handle. The back of the undercut should be perpendicular to the desired felling direction.

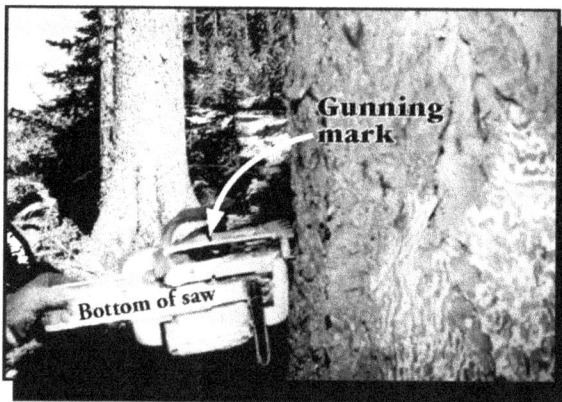

Figure 4-25—Use the gunning marks to check the felling direction.

If the tree is not aimed in the direction that you want it to fall, extend the horizontal and sloping cuts as needed, maintaining a single plane for each of the two cuts.

Back Cut and Wedging Procedures—The third cut needed to fell a tree is the back cut. The back cut can be made from either side of the tree if the saw has a full-wrap handlebar, as recommended in the *Health and Safety Code Handbook.* Choose the safest side of the tree to make the back cut.

In the area where you have removed the bark behind the horizontal cut, place the bumper spikes so the chain will cut no closer than 2 inches from the face and 2 inches above the face's horizontal cut. You may place the bumper spikes closer than 2 inches on smaller trees with lightweight tops.

The best way to envision these cuts is by the use of a rectangle (figure 4-26). The bottom corner is the back of the face's horizontal cut. The opposite upper corner will be the back of the back cut.

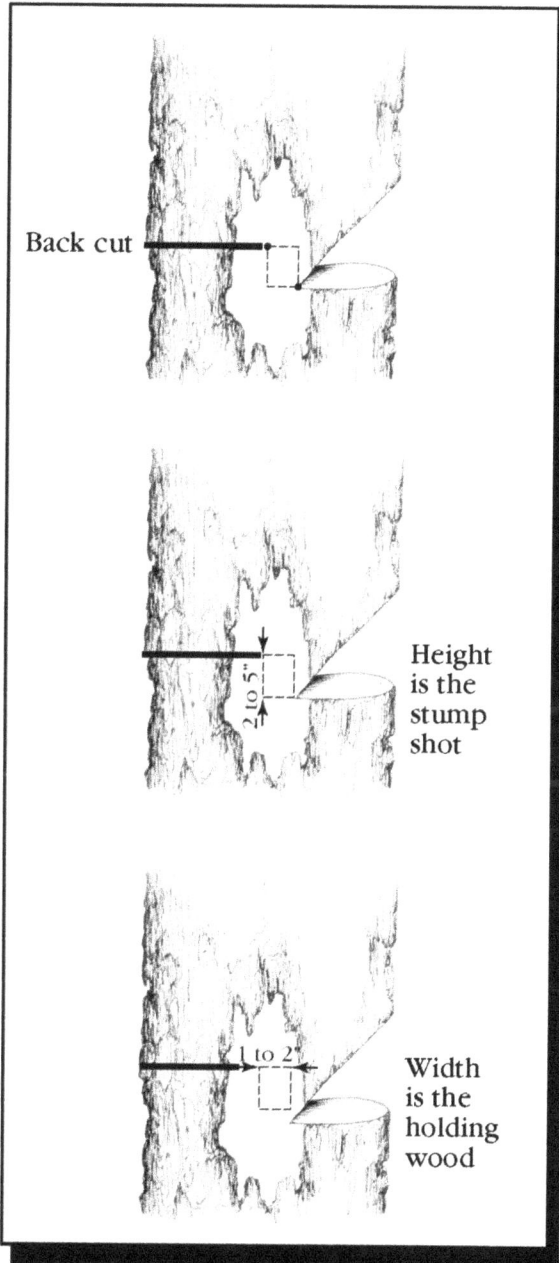

Figure 4-26—An imaginary rectangle can help the sawyer understand the importance of the back cut. The dimensions of this rectangle are based on a 24-inch-diameter tree.

The height of the rectangle is referred to as the stump shot. It is an antikickback device to prevent the tree from kicking back over the stump if it hits another tree during its fall. This is especially important when felling trees through standing timber.

The width of the rectangle is the holding wood. As the back cut is made, the sawyer must be careful not to cut this wood. Maintaining the holding wood is the key to safe and effective felling.

Start the back cut with the bumper spikes placed so the cut will end in the upper corner of the rectangle. Hold the saw level so that the back cut will be level. You want to be sure that when the cut is finished, it will line up with the top corner of the opposite rectangle. If the cut is angled, wedging power or the stump shot's height will be altered.

It may be helpful to cut or chop the bark to help level the bar. Do not cut deeper than the bark. Cuts into the wood will eliminate or reduce wedging lift. Once the cut has been made into the wood, do not change the cut's location.

Keep at least three wedges and an ax readily accessible while making the back cut. The wedges should be in a wedge holster worn on the waist. Keep the ax within arm's reach. The size of the wedge depends on the tree's diameter.

If there is any wind at all, at least two wedges are recommended. The second wedge adds stability. With only one wedge, the tree can set up a rocking action between the holding wood and the wedge. If a strong wind begins to blow, the holding wood can be torn out.

Remove thick bark immediately above and below the back cut's kerf where the wedges will be placed. The bark will compress, lessening the lifting power of the wedges.

Directional Felling

Place wedges in the kerf as soon as the chain and bar will permit. Place the wedges close together and parallel to the desired felling direction. Do not drive the wedges too hard. They will interfere with the back cut or cause the tree to become a heavy leaner.

Watch for the wedges to droop and occasionally try to push them in with your hands. Retighten them with an ax every 4 to 6 inches of cutting. The wedges are there in case the lean was incorrectly established, the wind causes the tree to set back, or the sawyer intends to fell the tree in a direction that differs from the tree's natural lean.

As you cut, continually look above for possible hazards and at the kerf for movement. Do not cut the holding wood.

The gunning marks can be used in reverse to help determine the guide bar's position. With the correct lean established and the proper relationship between the three cuts, the face will begin to close and the tree will fall in the planned direction.

Wedges must be used for all felling operations. Small trees limit the sawyer's use of wedges, even when small wedges are used.

A technique can be employed where half of the back cut is made at a time. This allows wedges to be placed without interfering with the guide bar.

After making the undercut, cut half of the back cut using the guide bar's tip. Make this cut from the tree's offside. Watch out for kickback and be careful not to cut the holding wood. Finish the back cut from the other side. Leave 1 to 2 inches of holding wood, depending on the diameter of the tree.

After removing the saw, place a small wedge in the kerf an inch or more from the remaining wood to be cut. Remember to keep the wedge tight but do not drive the wedge too hard. Finish the back cut using the tip of the guide bar, being prepared for kickback from the wedge. The wedge will be in position if the tree sits back. For trees that have a moderate amount of side lean, two wedges may be inserted on the side of the back cut that has been cut first (figure 4-27). As with other wedging operations, it is essential to tighten the wedges often, especially on trees that are attempting to sit back.

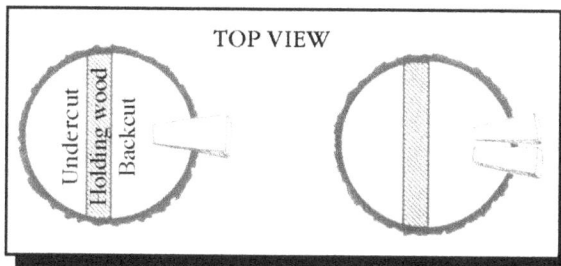

Figure 4-27—Wedges need to be parallel to the desired felling direction.

A sitback is a tree that settles back opposite the intended direction of fall during the back cut. Normally, this happens because the lean was incorrectly determined or the wind changed. If the sawyer has been following the proper felling procedure, there is a wedge in the back cut and the holding wood has been maintained. If the proper felling procedure has not been followed, the sawyer will need assistance because the tree is probably pinching the bar (figure 4-28).

Immediately notify your supervisor in the case of sitbacks and other felling difficulties. Before you leave a hazardous tree, be sure to mark the area clearly with flagging (figure 4-29) or with a written warning. Give a verbal warning to others working in the area. The supervisor shall reassess the tree and determine the skill level needed to fell the tree safely.

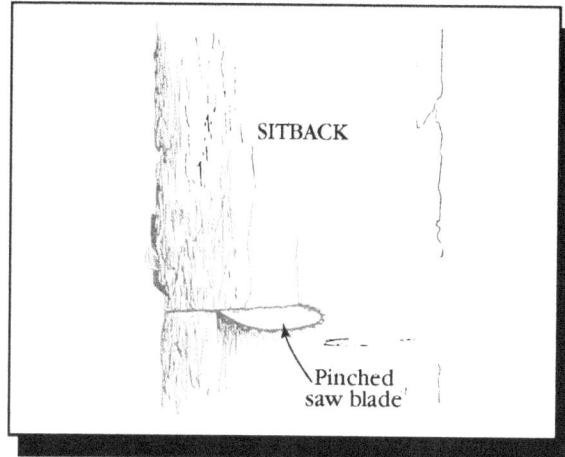

Figure 4-28—Sitback is when a tree settles back opposite the intended direction of fall.

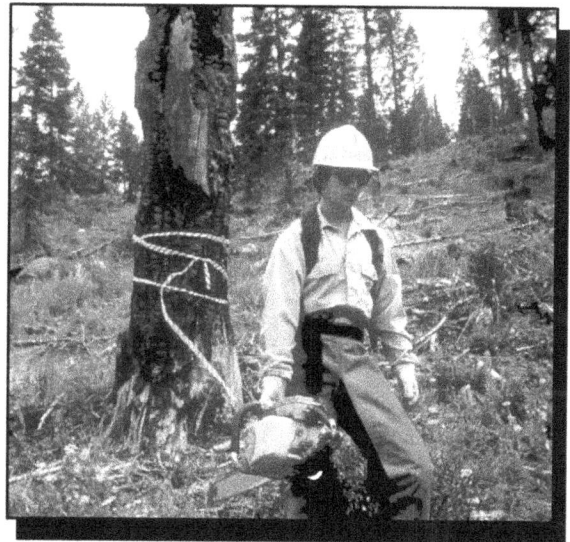

Figure 4-29—Clearly mark a hazard tree before leaving the area. Notify your supervisor of the hazard.

Snags also require careful attention to wedging. A snag is a standing dead tree, or portion of a tree, whose wood is decomposing. The steps for cutting a snag follow:

Shout a warning—Before working on a snag, everyone in the area must be notified. Remember, a snag can fall in any direction at any time.

Observe the top—Pay special attention to overhead hazards, branches, and the snag's top. Upper limbs may be weak and ready to come down at the least vibration. Never cut directly below a hazard. Look up while driving wedges.

Swamp out the base—Carefully check the condition of the bark on the snag. Loose bark can come sliding down the side of the snag and presents an extreme hazard to the sawyer. Standing back with room to escape, remove loose bark at the snag's base by prying it with an ax or a pole. Do not chop the bark, because this would set up vibration in the snag.

Size up the situation—Check the condition of wood by boring into it with the bar tip. Maintain the integrity of the holding wood. When sounding with an ax, look up while striking the tree. Check for frost cracks and other splits in the holding wood.

Determine two escape routes—Since the holding wood is rotten to some degree, you must establish two routes of escape.

Make the undercut—Do not fell a snag against its lean. Make the undercut and the back cut while standing upright. When you are standing, you can look up easily. In addition, you are in a position that allows immediate escape.

When you are cutting the undercut, be alert for the snag pinching the bar. Boring in the undercut area during sizeup should alert you to this possibility. Moving the bar back and forth will minimize the possibility of pinching. If the snag starts to sit on the bar, finish the undercut just to that depth. It is critical that the undercut has a wide opening and that it be cleaned out from corner to corner.

A short snag, with few or no limbs to give it lean, may need an undercut up to one-half the snag's diameter.

Felling Observers and Spotters

The use of personnel other than swampers in felling operations has been controversial. The *Health and Safety Code Handbook* states that if you choose to have additional personnel (such as during training), justification for the additional personnel and the implementation process shall be documented in the JHA.

Chapter 5—Crosscut Saw Tasks and Techniques (Suggested time: 2 hours)

Chapter objectives:

- Students will understand the different features of crosscut saws.
- Students will understand how a saw cuts and how the saw's components function.
- Students will test and assess a crosscut saw's performance, and recommend corrective measures.
- Students will recognize the various configurations of saw handles and their relationship to saw performance in various applications.
- Students will understand the value of a good saw maintenance program.
- Students will demonstrate how to properly sheathe and transport a saw.
- Students will learn the procedures for limbing, bucking, and felling.
- Students will understand the types of binds.

Historical Origin of the Crosscut Saw

The crosscut saw did not come into use until the 15th century. Early saws had a plain peg tooth design. Saws were used in Colonial America and were being manufactured in this country by the mid-1800's. Saws were not used for felling timber until around 1880. The machinery to make these vintage saws is no longer available. Crosscut saws manufactured today are lower quality.

Different Types of Crosscut Saws

Crosscut saws generally can be divided into two types: one- and two-person saws.

One-Person Crosscut Saws—A one-person crosscut saw's blade is asymmetrical. The saw has a D-shaped handle. The saw also has holes for a supplemental handle at the point (tip) and the butt (near the handle). The saws are usually 3 to 4½ feet long (figure 5-1).

Figure 5-1—One-person crosscut saw.

Two-Person Crosscut Saws—Two-person crosscut saws are symmetrical. They cut in either direction on the pull stroke. Vintage saws were made from 4 to 7 feet long in 6-inch increments.

Two-person crosscut saws (figure 5-2) manufactured today are flat ground. Most vintage saws were either straight taper, crescent taper, or flat ground. The saws have one or two holes, or a groove, on the ends of the blade where removable handles can be attached. Most vintage saws had teeth all the way to the ends of the blade. Saws manufactured today do not.

Figure 5-2—Two-person crosscut saw.

Two-Person Crosscut Saws

Felling Saws—Felling saws are best suited for felling standing timber. They cut best in a horizontal position. Felling saws have a concave back and are narrower than bucking saws (figure 5-3). The combination of a concave back and narrower width give felling saws the following characteristics:

- The saw is more flexible.
- The saw is lighter, so less effort is needed to use it.
- The sawyer can insert a wedge sooner.

Crosscut saws usually have two handles. Many vintage felling saws have one handle hole in each end.

Bucking Saws—Bucking saws can be used for felling. Some saws were manufactured to try to incorporate the best characteristics of both types of saws. Bucking saws have a straight back; they are much thicker than felling saws, so they are heavier and stiffer (see figure 5-3).

Because the bucking saw usually is operated by one person, it cuts on both the push and pull strokes. The saw's additional stiffness helps prevent the saw from buckling on the push stroke.

Because felling saws are flexible, they do not make a good bucking saw or a general all-around utility saw. The bucking saw is recommended as the standard saw for most trail and construction applications.

Figure 5-3—Comparison of felling and bucking saws. Concave-backed felling saws often have one handle hole per side. Straight-backed bucking saws can have two handle holes per side.

Saw Grinds

Historically, the sides of a saw were ground using one of three methods. Each method affected the thickness of the saw. These grinding methods are flat, straight taper, and crescent taper.

Flat Ground—On a flat-ground saw, the metal's thickness is the same throughout. Saws manufactured today are flat ground.

Straight Taper Ground—Straight taper-ground saws have an advantage over a flat-ground saw because the saw is thinner at the back than at the center (figure 5–4). The back of the saw has more clearance, reducing binding.

Straight taper-ground saw (not as likely to bind)

Flat-ground saw (tends to bind when cutting under compression)

Figure 5–4—Comparison of cuts made by straight taper-ground and flat-ground saws.

Straight taper-ground saws require less set. Set is the cutter tooth's offset from the plane of the saw.

Crescent Taper Ground—The best vintage saws were crescent taper ground (figure 5–5). Early saw manufacturing companies used different trade names for crescent taper-ground saws. The names included: crescent ground (Simonds), improved ground (Disston), and segment ground (Atkins).

End view | End view

Top edge

Top edge (exaggerated for clarity)

Each line represents uniform thickness, tapering from thick at teeth to thin at top.

STRAIGHT TAPER-GROUND SAW

CRESCENT TAPER-GROUND SAW

Figure 5–5—Comparison of straight taper-ground and crescent taper-ground saws. Neither is manufactured today. Today's saws are flat ground.

Crescent taper-ground saws offer the most clearance in the kerf of any of the grinds. These saws require the least amount of set, allowing the narrowest kerf. The thinnest part of a crescent taper-ground saw is at the back center.

How a Saw Cuts

A saw functions like a series of knives (teeth) making simultaneous parallel cuts and releasing the wood between them.

Cutter Teeth—All saws, regardless of the tooth pattern, are made up of two rows of cutting edges. The saw releases wood fibers on each side of the kerf as it passes through a log (figure 5-6).

Cutters work best in brittle, seasoned wood. The weakened fiber is easily removed.

Figure 5-6—How a crosscut saw cuts.

Rakers—Wet or green wood is hard to remove from the kerf because it is resilient. Even when the fiber is dislodged, it clogs a saw's cutter teeth.

A special kind of tooth, the raker, allows the cutter teeth to work more effectively with less effort. Even though the rakers do not sever fiber, they do perform the other two functions of saw teeth: breaking loose the cut fiber and removing it from the log. Rakers remove material whether the saw is being pushed or pulled.

Gullets—Wood fiber that has been severed must be stored by the saw while it is moved through the kerf and out of the cut. This storage area (the largest space between cutters or groups of cutters) is called a gullet.

The gullet must be large enough to store all the shavings until the gullet clears the log and the shavings fall free.

The gullets (figure 5-7) determine the proper length of saw for a given application. Example: A gullet in the

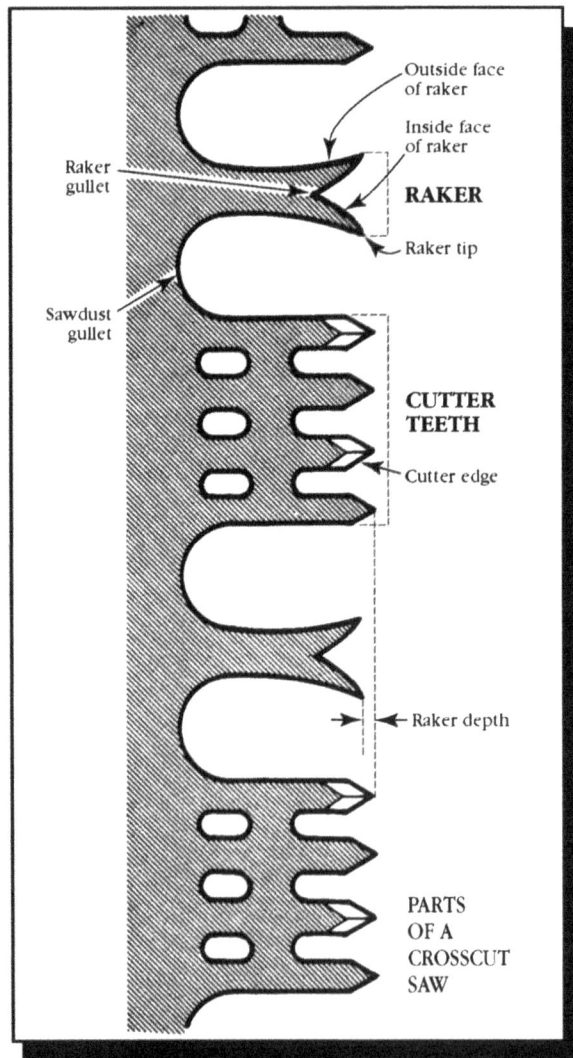

Figure 5-7—The configuration of the teeth of a crosscut saw. This is the perforated-lance tooth pattern.

middle of a 3-foot log must travel $1\frac{1}{2}$ feet to clear its shavings on either side. At the minimum, a $6\frac{1}{2}$- or 7-foot saw would be needed to provide this travel.

Tooth Patterns

For centuries, only the plain tooth (or peg tooth) pattern was used. Modifications to the plain tooth pattern were developed to make the work easier. We will discuss six patterns: the plain tooth, the M tooth, the Great American tooth, the champion tooth, the lance tooth, and the perforated lance tooth (figure 5–8).

Plain Tooth (Peg Tooth) Pattern—This pattern just includes cutter teeth. It is best used for cutting dry, very hard, or brittle small-diameter wood. Many bow saws and pruning saws use a plain tooth pattern.

M Tooth Pattern—This is the second generation of saw tooth patterns. The tooth pattern consists of pairs of teeth separated by a gullet. The outer edges of the teeth (the legs of the M) are vertical and act like rakers. The inside edges of the M are filed to a bevel, making a point. This tooth pattern is best suited for cutting dry, medium to hard woods.

Great American Tooth Pattern—This tooth pattern, three teeth separated by a gullet, is designed to cut dry, medium to hard woods. A special file is used to file these saws. The file can still be purchased today and is called a crosscut file or a Great American file.

Champion Tooth Pattern—This pattern is especially popular in the hardwood regions of North America. It consists of two alternately set cutter teeth and an unset raker with a gullet between them. The cutters are wider and more massive than the lance tooth pattern, allowing heavy sawing in extra hard, dry, or frozen wood. The

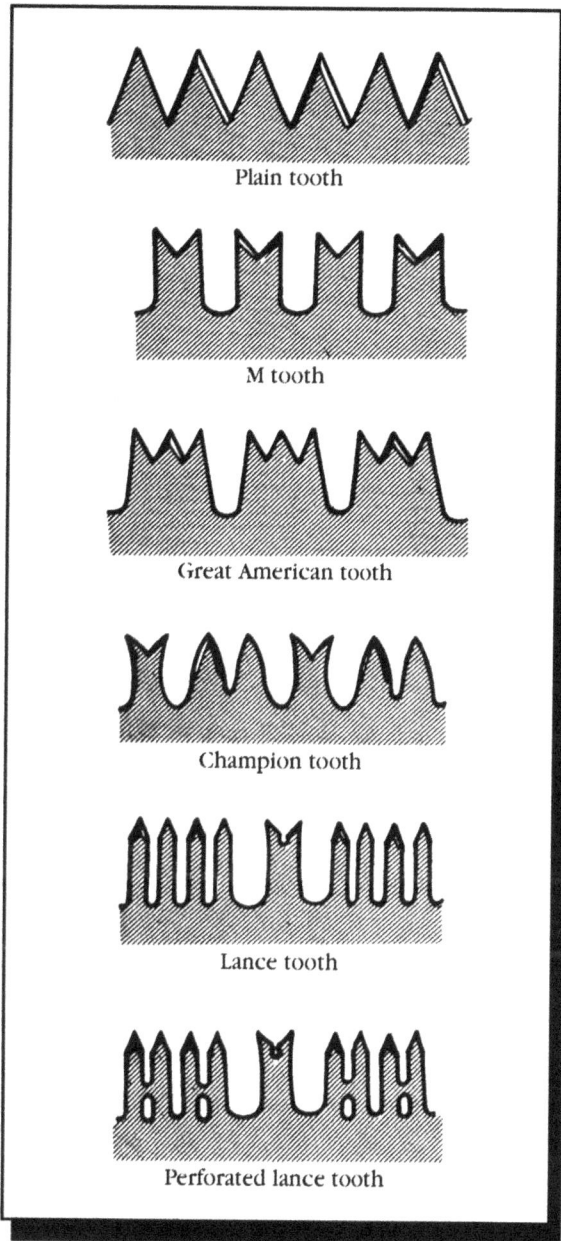

Figure 5–8—Saw tooth patterns.

larger teeth are sharpened in more of an almond shape rather than the pointed shape of a lance tooth.

Lance Tooth Pattern—For many years, the lance tooth pattern was the standard for felling and bucking timber in the American West. It consists of groups of four alternately set cutters separated by an unset raker with gullets on each side. The lance tooth pattern is best suited for cutting soft green timber, especially fir, spruce, and redwood.

Perforated Lance Tooth Pattern—This tooth pattern is considered a general utility pattern that can cut all but hard and frozen wood. It consists of groups of four alternately set cutters separated by an unset raker with gullets on each side. The bridges between the teeth form the perforations that give the pattern its name. These bridges strengthen the teeth and reduce chatter when the saw is used to cut harder wood.

Saw Handles

The handle's position on the saw affects the saw's efficiency. Changing either the arm and hand position, or the handle position, changes the delivery of force to the saw.

Types of Saw Handles

Handles may be fastened permanently to the blade with rivets. Removable handles may be fastened to the blade with a steel loop or with a pinned bolt and wingnut assembly.

Quality saw handles are often hard to find. Handles must be strong and must not allow movement between the handle and the blade.

Loop Style—The loop-style handle is a common design. Most of these models have a metal loop running up through a hardwood handle to a nut, which is inside the handle (plug nut) or is part of a cap at the end of the handle. The loop design allows the loop to be slipped

over the saw blade. When the wooden handle is turned, the loop tightens around the saw. These models do not use the saw handle holes. Most saws have a notch or a valley that the bottom of the loop rests in.

Because these saw blades must have a notch for the loop, they do not have teeth all the way to the end of the blade.

Pin Style—The pin-style handle design—the most common—uses the handle holes in the saw blade.

The climax-style handles were the most common pin-style design. Even today, they appear on some modern two-person crosscut saws.

Perhaps the most common vintage saw handle used today is the Pacific Coast model of the pin-style design. It has a finger guard with a groove to accept the saw blade and two cast flanges. The ½-inch-diameter rivet pin passes through a hole in the wooden handle. It is secured with a heavy wingnut.

Supplementary handles are used on one-person crosscut saws. The handle can be placed at the end of the saw for an additional sawyer or directly in front of the D-shaped handle when a single sawyer wants to use both hands.

Handle Installation and Maintenance

A one-person saw has a fixed D-shaped handle with additional holes on the top of the saw to attach a supplemental handle. Many two-person crosscut saws (usually bucking saws) have two holes on each end for handles. Moving the handle from the lower hole has the same effect as moving the hands several inches up the saw handle. With the handle in the upper hole, a push stroke applies more downward force on the saw, causing the teeth to sink deeper into the wood. The deeper cut requires more force on the pull stroke. A slight upward force is applied to the saw, making it easier to pull.

The wooden handles on crosscut saws are usually select-grade hardwoods 1¼ inches in diameter and about 14 inches long. When the handle is not on the saw, the handle needs to be kept away from sharp edges that could nick or cut it.

Saw Maintenance

The maintenance topics discussed in this section are for the crosscut sawyer. Some topics, such as saw filing, are included just to provide an overview during training. An experienced saw filer should do the filing. The *Crosscut Saw Manual* (7771-2508-MTDC, revised 2003) by Warren Miller is an excellent resource for more information on saw maintenance and filing.

Cleaning the Saw

Saws need to be clean to function effectively. Clean saws at the end of the day before storing them.

Lubricants and Solvents—*Types:* Petroleum-free lubricants, such as canola oil, are available commercially. Solvents with citrus-based ingredients, such as Citro-squeeze, also are recommended.

Functions: Saw teeth do not need to be lubricated as they cut. The friction of the saw teeth against the kerf keeps the teeth reasonably clean. However, resin deposits on the lower part of the teeth and in the saw gullets produce drag. Lubricants can soften these deposits and help remove them.

Cutting in extremely wet environments or during a hard rain can cause wood fibers to swell. In these conditions, a petroleum-free lubricant can help reduce drag. Clean the saw with an environmentally acceptable solvent at

the end of each day and apply a thin coat of petroleum-free lubricant.

Applying Lubricants: Open containers waste lubricants. Squeeze bottles allow the sawyer to direct a stream of lubricant onto the saw's surface. On the pull stroke, the sawyer keeps one hand on the saw handle and applies the lubricant with the other, putting the bottle down before the next push stroke.

Removing Rust: Rust probably does more damage to saws than anything else. Remove light rust using steel wool. Use a pumice grill block to remove rust that is too heavy to be removed with steel wool. A liberal amount of cleaning solution will keep the block's pores open.

To remove heavier rust, use an ax stone. Always use a liberal amount of cleaning solution. *NEVER* use a dry stone on the saw blade.

As rust and other deposits are removed, you will see imperfections in the saw blade. Spots that are shinier than the rest of the saw are high spots. Spots that are duller than the normal saw surface indicate low spots. A high spot on one side of the blade usually produces a low spot on the other side. These kinks or bends need to be hammered out by an experienced saw filer.

Do not apply too much pressure on the cutter teeth because you can remove metal from the set and reduce tooth length.

A wire brush can be used to remove loose rust and scale. *NEVER* use a power sanding disk on a saw blade.

Removing Pitch: A saw that is well cared for will not rust, but it will develop pitch deposits during normal use. Some pitch can be removed with a citrus-based solvent as the saw is being used by allowing the saw's motion to scrub away the buildup. However, pitch still can be deposited on the saw. Pitch buildups can be removed at the end of the day with steel wool and a cleaning solution.

Using Cleaning Solutions: Limit the use of harsh chemicals for cleaning saws. Wear the proper personal protective equipment and know how to use the cleaning solutions safely. Check the material safety data sheet if you are unfamiliar with the hazards of using and storing a particular product. A number of citrus-based cleaners on the market are effective and safe.

Naval gel can be applied to remove heavy rust and scale. Use only as directed, with adequate ventilation. This product stops the chemical reaction of the rust.

Checking for Straightness

Check the saw periodically for straightness. A saw should be checked if it receives any harsh treatment during transportation or use. A saw that is not straight can buckle on the push stroke. The narrower, lighter felling saws are more prone to buckling.

Using Straightedges—Remove the saw handles and hang the saw vertically from one of its handle holes.

Saw filers usually have straightedges made especially for this work. You will need a pair of straightedges. Two combination square rules can be used. Before using the straightedges on the saw, hold them together and make sure they maintain contact along their entire length. You should not see light between them when you put them together and hold them up to a light source.

Straightedges work by allowing you to feel the difference in resistance between the saw and the straightedge as the straightedges are twisted back and forth over the saw's surface. The straightedges are moved as a pair with the saw between them. You will feel increased drag on the ends of the straightedge on the side of a saw with a depression. On the other side of the saw, the straightedge

will pivot easily on the corresponding bump. Even resistance on both straightedges reflects a straight saw that does not have any kinks, bends, or bumps.

If you find any major irregularities, report them to the person who files your saws.

Testing the Saw—Testing determines whether a saw cuts straight, runs smooth, and produces long, thick shavings. The saw should produce shavings and not sawdust. The longer and more abundant the shavings, the better the saw is performing. Green logs produce longer shavings than dry logs. The shavings should be long and thick with smooth edges. If the edges of the shavings have whiskers or irregularities, the rakers are probably too long. If the shavings are paper thin, the rakers are too short (figure 5-9).

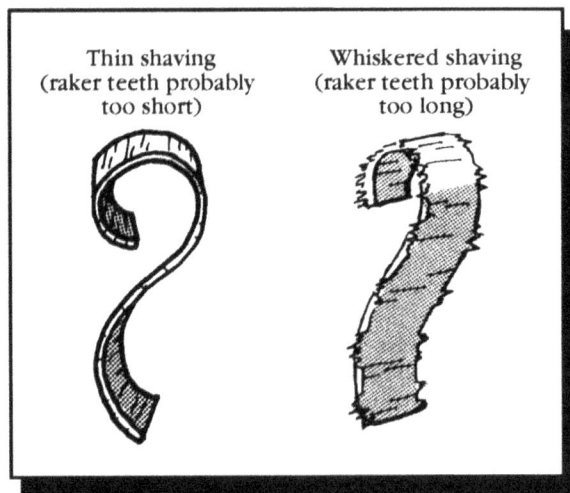

Figure 5-9—Examine shavings to identify sharpening problems.

Does the saw cut straight? Cut far enough into the test log to determine whether the cut is perfectly straight. If the saw consistently pulls to one side through no fault of the sawyer, the saw needs additional maintenance.

Sometimes a sawyer standing in an awkward position can put a twist or bend on the saw. A saw will not cut straight if it is kinked or bent.

back of the saw

circle of the saw

toothed edge

Long-Term Storage: Store crosscut saws straight. Remove the handles and store the saws in a dry location.

NEVER store a saw flat on a metal surface. It is best to hang a saw from a nail through a handle hole. Although the saw can lie horizontally if it is supported along its entire length, items may be dropped on the saw, damaging it. During long-term storage, oil will bleed into the saw's wooden handle if the saw is lying flat.

Apply a coating of heavy oil or grease diluted with solvent before storing a saw. Wear appropriate gloves when applying the oil.

NEVER lean a saw against a wall where it could develop a bend.

NEVER leave a saw bent around a fire pack.

DO NOT store a saw in a sheath or with a guard on it. Rubber-lined fire hose is particularly bad because it traps moisture next to the saw's teeth.

DO NOT hang a saw where animals or people could be injured by the saw's unsheathed teeth.

DO NOT store saws on top of one another. When the unsheathed saws rub against each other, the saws can be damaged.

Storage in the field: Saws need to be wiped clean and rubbed with canola oil or another environmentally sensitive lubricant before you leave them in the field. Choose a storage location out of human sight and away from game trails. If saws are being left overnight, they can be laid under a log with the teeth pointed in.

Remove the saw handles and sheaths. Bears tend to gnaw on wooden handles. Rodents chew on leather straps and anything that has salt on it. Leave nothing but the metal parts in the field. If you are storing a saw longer than for just one night, hang it.

Saw sheaths: Sheaths protect the saw and prevent it from causing damage or inflicting injury. Saws should be sheathed as much as possible unless they are being used or are in storage. Wear gloves when removing or replacing a saw sheath.

A length of old firehose that has been split makes one of the best crosscut saw sheaths. Wipe the hose's rubber inner lining with an oily rag to repel water and reduce the possibility that moisture in the sheath will cause the saw to rust.

Attach the firehose to the saw using parachute cord or Velcro closures. To install the hose sheath, begin by rolling it inside out (rubber side out). Turn the saw so its teeth face up; unroll the hose down the saw, covering the teeth.

Some sawyers sandwich the saw between two rectangular pieces of plywood. The saw's handle holes are placed over pins at each end of one of the pieces of plywood, securing the saw.

Transporting Saws—Saws must be transported in a way that protects them from being damaged, from injuring people or livestock, and from damaging property and equipment.

Saws are difficult to transport because they are long and flexible. Vintage saws are bent to make them easier for hikers or packstock to carry. Saws can be delivered by parachute. Modern saws *SHOULD NOT BE BENT.* The softer metal will hold the bend.

Because saws may be taken by boat, plane, helicopter, truck, dog sled, or packstock, or be carried by a hiker during different legs of a journey, several types of protection may be needed to get a saw to the work site. Sheaths should always cover saws when they are being transported.

Saws get hot in the sun. Use gloves to handle a saw that has been lying in the sun.

Boats: If a saw is being transported in an open skiff, remove the saw's handles and place the sheathed saw on top of the other cargo. On many boats, the place that is the most out of the way is along the gunwales. Open boats can take on a lot of spray. Saltwater spray can cause rust. ALWAYS coat the saw with canola oil or another environmentally sensitive lubricant before transporting it. Once the saw is on land, remove the sheath and rinse off any salt with a good freshwater bath.

Saws transported on kayaks are best secured to the bow where they can be seen. In canoes, carry saws in the center on the floor. Transport the saw without handles in a rubber-lined hose sheath. Secure the saw by tying parachute cord through the handle holes. Be sure to remove the sheath and dry the saw after arriving at your destination.

Aircraft: In small aircraft, the saw's handles can get in the way. If a saw's handles must be removed to bend the saw into a loop, wire *MUST* be strung through the handle holes to secure the saws. *DO NOT* string parachute cord or any other nonmetallic material (including nylon ties) through the handle holes to secure the saw. Jostling during the flight could cut nonmetallic materials, allowing the saw to spring to full length. The same considerations apply when saws are carried in helicopters.

Helicopters can transport saws as an external load. Use care when packing saws that are carried as sling loads by helicopters. One way to reduce breakage is to carefully bend the saw around a box. Place the box in the middle of the sling bag with the saw's ends down. Stack other materials around the saw.

Vehicles: When transporting crosscut saws in a pickup truck, lay the sheathed saw flat on the bed of the truck. Don't place heavy tools on top of the saw.

Dog Sleds: In some areas, saws are transported by dog sled. If you do not expect to use the saw to clear trails during the trip, sheathe the saw and place it on the bottom of the sled. If the saw may be needed for trail work, place it along one side of the sled where it will be easier to reach.

Packstock: Take extra care when carrying a crosscut saw on packstock. Select the gentlest animal to carry the saw. Put that animal in the lead where you can see the saw easily.

The handles on a two-person saw shall remain attached. Sheathe the saw with firehose and wrap the saw in a mantie with the handles exposed and secure. Bend and place the saw over the animal with the teeth facing to the rear (figure 5-11). Tie the saw handles down to the latigo or the cinch ring. Tie the center of the bowed saw to the packsaddle and not just to the load. When the saw is fastened on top, it is more likely to stay on top of the animal if the rope on either side becomes untied. Finish the packing job by using the cinch lash to tie the saw to the rest of the load. That way, the saw is unlikely to come loose.

Figure 5-11—Bend and place the saw over the animal with the teeth facing to the rear.

One-person saws can be transported on riding stock in a leather or canvas scabbard (similar to a rifle scabbard). A piece of hardwood protects the scabbard from the saw's teeth.

Hikers: Saws should be sheathed when you are hiking to the job site. The person carrying the saw should be the last person in line.

Two-person saws should have the rear handle removed. If the handle is left on, it can snag on branches.

The saw can be carried on your shoulder with the teeth facing outward. AVOID carrying the saw with the teeth pointing inward. Carry the saw on your downhill shoulder so you can throw it off if you slip or fall.

A vintage saw can be bent around a pack if it is being carried for long distances. Usually, both handles are left on to secure the saw in its bent position.

Saw-Related Equipment and Tools

Axes

Single-bit axes need to be heavy enough (3 to 5 pounds) to drive plastic wedges into the trees being felled. The back of the ax (poll) should be smooth, have rounded edges, and be free of burrs to minimize damage to wedges. Pulaskis should never be used to drive wedges.

Always remove branches, underbrush, overhead obstructions, or debris that might interfere with limbing and chopping. Do not allow anyone to stand in the immediate area. Make sure workers know how far materials may fly. Protect all workers against flying chips and other chop-ping hazards by requiring them to wear the appropriate PPE.

Always position your body securely while working with a tool. Never chop crosshanded; always use a natural striking action. Be alert when working on hill-sides or uneven ground. If you cut a sapling that is held down by a fallen log, the sapling may spring back. Be alert for sudden breakage. If you do not have a need to cut something, leave it alone.

Never use chopping tools as wedges or mauls. Do not allow two persons to chop or drive wedges together on the same tree. When chopping limbs from a felled tree, stand on the opposite side of the log from the limb being chopped and swing toward the top of the tree or branch. Do not allow the tool handle to drop below a plane that is parallel with the ground unless you are chopping on the side of the tree opposite your body.

If the cutting edge picks up a wood chip, stop. Remove the chip before continuing. To prevent blows from glanc-ing, keep the striking angle of the tool head perpendicu-lar to the tree trunk.

Wedges

The use of wedges differs when cutting with a crosscut saw rather than a chain saw.

Wedges are essential tools for safe felling and bucking. They provide a way to lift the tree, preventing the tree from sitting back when it is being felled. A wedge must be inserted into the back cut as soon as possible. Wedges also reduce binds on the saw when bucking.

Select the correct wedge for the job. The proper type, size, and length of a wedge vary, depending on the wedge's use. The size of the tree being felled or the material being bucked determines the size of the wedge that will be needed. If the wedge is too small, it may be ineffective.

Most wedges are made out of plastic or soft metal, such as magnesium, and come in different sizes. Use plastic wedges in both felling and bucking operations to prevent damaging the saw if it contacts the wedges. Plastic wedges do not split easily, and their textured surfaces provide additional holding power in the wood, helping to prevent the wedges from backing out when they are being driven.

Although all wedges can be stacked (used one on top of the other), wedges may slip sideways if each wedge is not driven squarely. Always drive wedges by striking them squarely on the head. Drive them carefully to keep them from flying out of the cut.

Newer wedge designs include *rifled* wedges. These wedges have a pair of grooves on one side and rails on the other side. This design helps the wedges stay in place when they are stacked on each other.

The two basic types of wedges used in sawing are single (figure 5-12) and double (figure 5-13) taper. The triple-taper wedge (figure 5-14) has a thin angle at the entry,

Figure 5-13—Double-taper wedges are designed to reduce bind.

Figure 5-14—Triple-taper wedges allow a short wedge to provide as much lift as a longer wedge but require more force to drive.

an intermediate angle through most of the body, and a steeper angle near the top. This design allows a shorter wedge to produce as much lift as a longer single-taper wedge and works well on small-diameter trees.

Check wedges daily or before each job. Do not use cracked or flawed wedges. Wedges that are damaged need to be cleaned up before they are used again.

Recondition heads and the tapered ends when grinding wedges to the manufacturer's original shape and angle. Wear eye protection and a dust mask when grinding.

Repair any driving tool or remove it from service when its head begins to chip or mushroom.

Carry wedges in a wedge holster or other container, not in the pockets of clothing.

Splitting Wedges—Splitting wedges are made of steel. Magnesium wedges should not be used to split wood.

Figure 5-12—A rifled single-taper wedge is designed to provide lift when a tree is felled. It can be stacked with additional rifled single-taper wedges. The rifling helps keep the wedges aligned and stacked as they are being driven.

Steel wedges with smooth faces sometimes rebound out of cuts when they are driven. Smooth faces can be roughened up with a cold chisel. Most steel wedges have shallow grooves or depressions below the wedge face. Wood fills these voids and reduces the chance that the wedge might back out.

Wedges must be set firmly before they are driven with a double-jack sledge hammer.

Wedges to reduce bind or split wood are double-tapered, meaning that each of the broad faces taper equally from the center. When such wedges are driven, the force is equal on both sides, causing the wood to move equally.

Lifting Wedges—Lifting wedges are an inclined plane, tapered on just one face.

Lifting wedges exert force in the direction of the inclined plane. Two wedges can be stacked one on top of the other to produce an even lift. Lifting wedges have many applications. They can be used to tighten, pry apart, or move materials.

Exerting a force in one direction can be valuable. The sawyer may need to exert a force in one direction when getting a saw unstuck or when removing a chunk of log if a carelessly placed compound cut gets bound up.

Plastic or steel wedges can be bought with a single taper. These wedges often have a groove on the flat side to increase holding power. The lifting or moving takes place on the smooth side that serves as the inclined plane.

Peaveys and Cant Hooks

The blacksmith Joseph Peavey invented the peavey (see figure 3-23a). Both the peavey and the cant hook (see figure 3-23b) use a curved metal hook on the end of a straight handle to roll or skid logs. A peavey has a sharp pointed spike at the lower end, while a cant hook has a

tow or lip. Most peaveys and cant hooks come with a duckbill hook that is a good all-around style. Peaveys and cant hooks have hickory handles that are from 2 to 5½ feet long.

Peaveys are used almost exclusively in the woods. Peaveys are handy for prying logs up onto blocks to keep the saw from pinching while bucking. The cant hook is used primarily to roll logs.

- Keep the handles free of splinters, splits, and cracks.
- Keep points sharp.
- Keep your body balanced when pushing or pulling the pole.
- Grip the handle firmly; do not overstress it.
- Place a guard on the point when the tool is not in use.

Underbucks

Underbucks help hold the saw in position when the saw is cutting from underneath the log. They also act as a fulcrum. A good sawyer can cut as fast—or faster—from underneath a log as from the top. When a sawyer is cutting from underneath, a downward pressure on the underbuck handle forces the saw up into the log. The sawyer does not have that mechanical advantage when cutting from the top.

Types of Underbucks—Axes are the most common type of underbuck. Axes used for underbucking should have a 36-inch wooden handle that has been slightly modified. Cut two series of three notches on one side of the handle about 6 inches from the end, leaving room (below the notches) for your gripping hand when you use the ax for chopping.

The three notches, placed about an inch apart, allow the sawyer to more accurately line up one of the notches with the cut. The notches should be 30 to 45 degrees off perpendicular to allow room for the saw between the ax handle and the log.

Some mechanical underbucks attach to axes; others are sheaves that fit over an ax handle; and others are stand-alone tools. Most underbucks have a groove or roller on the end to serve as a guide for the back of the saw (figure 5-15). This groove or roller needs to be adjusted properly to align the saw cut.

Figure 5-15—A mechanical underbuck helps hold the saw up when cutting from the underside of the log.

The MTDC tech tip, *Crosscut Saw Underbucking Tool* (0223-2330-MTDC), shows how to fabricate a lightweight underbuck that features a 2-inch clamp with a shielded steel pulley. It attaches to an ax handle.

Bucking Preparation and Techniques

Safety Considerations

The same principles apply whether a crosscut saw or a chain saw is used for bucking, but the sawyer is exposed to risks longer during crosscut saw operations. Great care needs to be taken when bucking.

Situational Awareness:
- Never buck a tree that exceeds your ability.
- Consider overhead hazards.
- Establish good footing.

- Swamp out bucking areas and escape routes.
- Anticipate what will happen when the log is cut.
- Plan the bucking cut carefully after considering:
  —*Slope.* People and property in the cutting zone can be in the path of rolling logs.
  —*Tension.* Spring poles are trees under tension.
  —*Compression.* Falling or rolling root wads are unpredictable when compression is released.
  —*Rocks and foreign objects under the log.* The log will have a tendency to roll, slide, or bind. Broken off limbs hidden underneath the log can roll up and strike the sawyer.

Bucking Sizeup

Three major hazards are associated with bucking.

Spring Poles—Spring poles are generally small-diameter trees or brush that are pinned under larger trees (figure 5-16). Because the trees or brush are still rooted, when they become pinned, they are under tension. If this tension is undetected, when the spring poles are cut, they can spring back with tremendous force and strike the sawyer. Cut a spring pole only when necessary.

Determine what will happen when the spring pole is cut. A crosscut saw is not used to release a spring pole unless the pole is very large. Normally an ax, pruning saw, or pulaski is used.

Figure 5-16— Look for spring poles. They can release and cause accidents.

• To remove spring poles properly, begin by relieving some of the tension in a controlled manner. To do this, stand back at a safe distance and make a series of shallow cuts about one-half inch apart on the underside of the spring pole. Be careful not to cut too deep. During each cut, as soon as you detect movement, remove the saw and begin the next cut. Four to six cuts on the bottom of the spring pole should be sufficient.

• The release cut is made from the top, about ½ inch past the end of the series of cuts on the bottom and on the piece that is going to fall to the ground. Be sure you are clear of the piece that will be released.

Suspended Logs—Cutting a suspended log is a single-buck operation. Often only one side is safe or has adequate footing for you to make the cut.

If you are standing on blowdown where several trees are jackstrawed in different directions, carefully evaluate the sequence in which trees should be removed. Generally, ***REMOVE THE BOTTOM LOGS FIRST***. This practice reduces the chance that top logs or other material will move.

It might not be possible to remove all suspended trees with a saw. Only take out the ones that can be removed safely. Other suspended trees can be removed with winches or explosives, if necessary.

Suspended logs often roll when they are released. Be sure the log has a safe path to travel. Logs may ricochet off other objects, making their path unpredictable. ***BE SURE*** no snags or other weak trees are in the log's path. They could snap if they were struck by a rolling log. Fell snags or weak trees first, if they can be felled safely.

Unsound Wood—Unsound wood can crack or break without warning. It can be hazardous because it is unpredictable. Logs may be sound in one area and rotten in other areas. Examine ends of logs for signs of rot. Observe the color of shavings the saw is producing. Dark shavings indicate rot. Rotten wood doesn't hold wedges well, making them ineffective. Because rotten logs may hold more moisture, crosscut saws tend to load up, increasing the need to use wedges to keep the kerf open.

Planning the Cut

Can the log be safely bucked with the sawyer's skills and equipment? Sawyers should not feel pressured to perform any task that is above their ability. Ask other crew members to size up the situation silently. Discuss findings afterward.

Types of Cuts—The three basic types of cuts are straight cuts, compound cuts, and offset cuts. We will describe each type of cut and its usual application (figure 5-17).

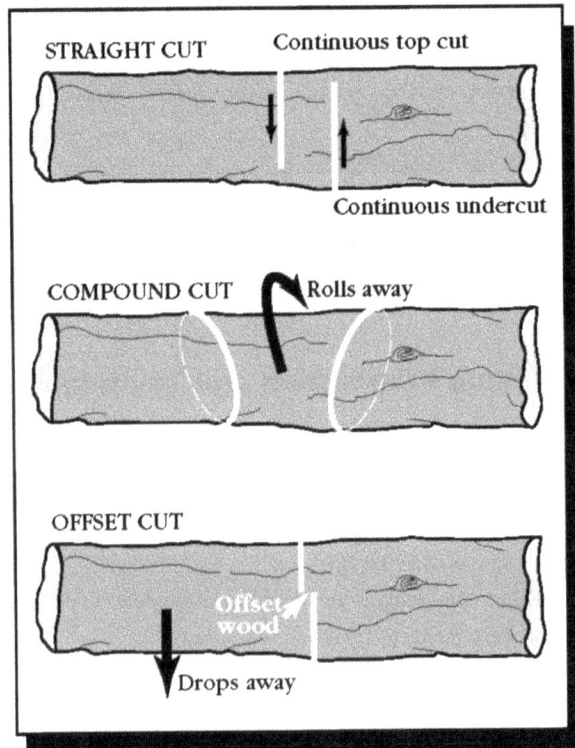

Figure 5-17—Three basic cuts: straight, compound, and offset.

A *straight cut* is made through the log from one side. It can be performed by single or double bucking. It also can be cut from underneath the log by a single sawyer (using an underbuck).

A *compound cut* is placed at an angle less than perpendicular to the log and angled so that the bottom of the cut slopes toward the part of the log that is being removed. This cut typically is used when clearing a large log that is across a trail. Two cuts need to be made and the severed chunk of the log has to be removed.

The *offset cut* is placed so that the bottom underbucking cut **DOES NOT MATCH UP** exactly with the top cut. This kind of underbucking operation is used when a log is suspended and will drop free when severed. Once the top cut has been made, a single sawyer installs a mechanical underbuck or selects one of the grooves cut into the ax handle (a groove about ½ inch toward the ax head from the top kerf). The ax head is always secured to the side of the log that won't move when the log is cut.

The small amount of offset wood acts like the holding wood left when trees are felled. In felling, the holding wood keeps the tree from kicking back. In underbucking, the offset wood prevents the severed log from damaging the saw when the log drops. If the offset wood is severed, control is lost. If the cuts meet, the log will want to carry the saw with it when the log drops. Because the ax handle supports the saw, the saw's force can break the ax handle. The saw may fly upward, possibly injuring the sawyer, or bending, kinking, or snapping the saw.

Determining Binds—Understanding directional pressures, or binds, is important. These binds determine bucking techniques and procedures.

Landforms, stumps, blowdown, and other obstacles that prevent a log from lying flat cause binds. Binds are different directional pressures exerted in different areas of the log. The tension area (figure 5-18) is the portion of the log where the wood fibers are being stretched apart. In this portion of the log, the saw's cut (kerf) opens as the cut is made. In the compression area, the wood fibers push together. In this portion of the log, the kerf closes as the cut is made.

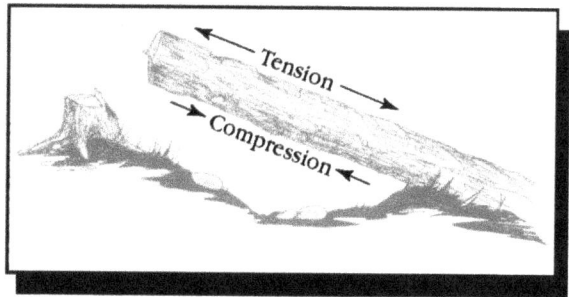

Figure 5-18—The log is being pulled apart by tension force and pushed together by compression force. The tension and compression areas are on opposite sides of the log.

It is extremely important to determine what will happen to the log when it is cut. Inspect the log for all binds, pivot points, and natural skids. Various bucking techniques can be used to lower a suspended tree to the ground.

The four types of bind are: top, bottom, side, and end (figure 5-19). Normally, logs have a combination of two or more binds:

Top bind: The tension area is on the bottom of the log. The compression area is on the top.

Bottom bind: The tension area is on the top of the log. The compression area is on the bottom.

Side bind: Pressure is exerted sideways on the log.

End bind: Weight compresses the log's entire cross section.

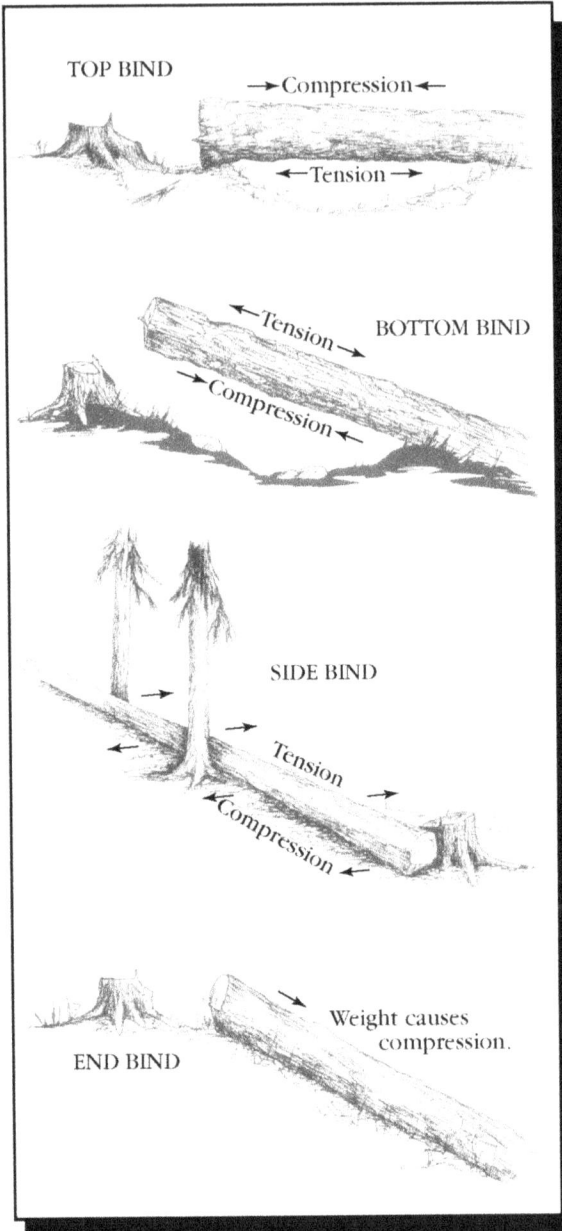

Figure 5-19—There are four types of binds. A log can have a combination of two or more binds.

Determine Bucking Locations—It is best to start bucking at the top of the log and work toward the butt end, removing the binds in smaller material first. Look for broken limbs and tops above the working area. *NEVER* stand under an overhead hazard while bucking.

Look for spring poles—Look for small trees and limbs bent under the log being bucked. They may spring up as the log rolls away. If you can safely do so, cut them off before the log is bucked. Otherwise, move to a new cutting location and flag the hazard. Anticipate the spring poles' reactions.

Determine the Offside—The offside (figure 5-20) is the side the log might move to when it is cut, normally the downhill side. Watch out for possible pivots. Clear the work area and escape route. Establish solid footing and remove debris that may hinder your escape.

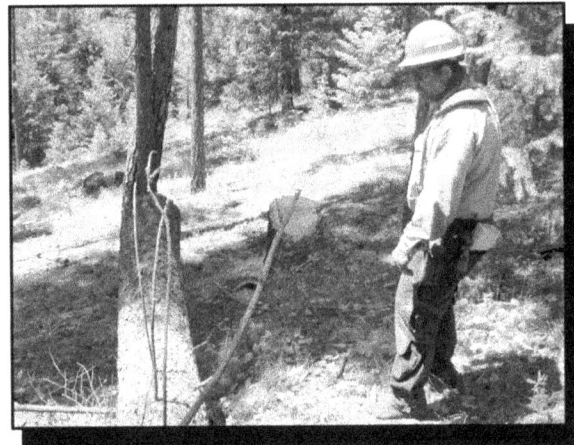

Figure 5-20—Determine the offside (usually the downhill side) and stay clear of that side when you are single bucking.

Cut the Offside First From a Safe Position—If possible, make a cut about one-third the diameter of the log. This allows the sawyer to step back from the log on the final cut.

Watch the Kerf To Detect Log Movement—Position yourself so you can detect a slight opening or closing of the kerf. There is no better indicator of the log's reaction on the release cut. If the bind cannot be evaluated, proceed with caution. It may be necessary to move the saw back and forth slowly to prevent the saw from getting bound as pressure closes the kerf. Cut only far enough to place a wedge. Continue cutting. Watch the kerf. If the kerf starts to open, the log has a bottom bind. If the kerf starts to close, the log has a top bind (figure 5-21).

Figure 5-21—Watch the kerf for movement that will indicate a bottom bind (kerf opens) or top bind (kerf closes).

Reduce the Remaining Wood—Visually project the kerf's location to the bottom of the log. Cut a short distance into the log along this line to reduce the amount of wood to be cut on the final cut. Be prepared for kickback.

Hazards of Bucking in Blowdown—Strong winds uprooted trees in areas of blowdown. At any time while the bucking cuts are being made, the roots can drop back into place or roll in any direction. Avoid standing directly behind or downhill from the roots.

Small trees growing on the roots of blowdown (figure 5-22) could be forced into the sawyer's position if the

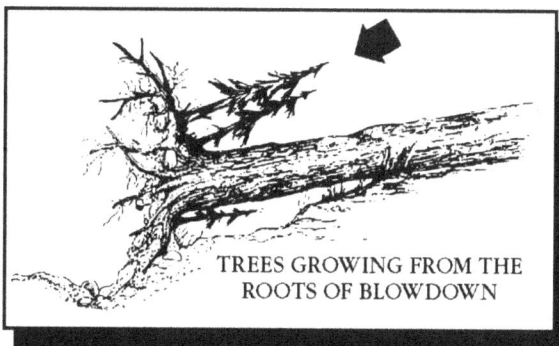

Figure 5-22—Small trees growing on the roots of blowdown (arrow) can move if the roots drop or roll.

roots drop or roll. Cut the small trees off first. Some of the trees' limbs may be preventing the roots from rolling. Don't cut off those limbs.

Points to Remember

- Size up your situation thoroughly. Identify the hazards and establish your escape routes and safety zones.
- Use objects such as rocks, stumps (if they are tall enough), and sound, standing trees with no overhead hazards for protection in the event the tree springs sideways toward you when you saw the release cut.
- Eliminate other binds before removing any single section of log that may be under stress. Angled bucking cuts, wide on top and made on the offside, allow a single section of log to be removed. Angled cuts let the bucked section of log roll away from the rest of the log. Buck small sections that will be easy to control when they begin moving.
- Reevaluate your situation constantly, because binds and log movement will change as you cut.
- Approach a cutting operation only from the uphill side. Warn workers who are working in and below an active cutting area. Allow workers time to move to a safe area. Verify their safety visually and verbally. Announce when a bucking operation has been completed.
- Sever all logs completely as you buck. Partially bucked logs are hazards and should be marked with flagging.

Single-Bucking Techniques

New sawyers should master the skill of single bucking before learning double bucking. If new sawyers can handle a long two-person saw alone, they have mastered the principles of keeping the saw running smoothly without buckling. Thinner, lighter felling saws are hard for all but the most experienced sawyers to use for single bucking. The stiffer, heavier bucking saw is easier to push during single-bucking.

The reasons to single buck are:

- The sawyer starts out double bucking and needs to finish the cut from one side because of safety considerations or log movement.
- The log is too large for the length of the saw.
- The sawing sequence starts or ends with underbucking, which can be done only by a single sawyer.

As a general rule, the saw needs to be twice as long as the log's diameter plus 6 inches. To illustrate the problem, imagine trying to cut a 4-foot-diameter log with a 7-foot saw. If the center raker and adjoining gullets are in the center of the log, each sawyer needs at least 2 feet of free blade so the center gullets will clear the log. With a 7-foot saw, the shavings would never be removed from the gullets in the center foot of the saw. On each stroke, the gullets would pick up more shavings. As the gullets filled, the saw would work harder and bind, especially if the wood was green and pitchy. Usually, sawyers can't run the saw all the way to the handles without having their hands drawn into the bark.

A single sawyer can take off the handle at one end of the saw. That end of the saw can be drawn into the log, allowing the shavings to be removed from the gullets.

When making compound cuts, the length of the cut determines how long the saw needs to be. The saw does not work as efficiently in a sloping cut or a compound cut. The more angle that is placed on a compound cut, the less effective the saw is working. Compound cuts can make for some hard sawing.

Single Bucking with No Bind: Top Cutting—
- Lay the unsheathed saw on its side over the log to be bucked. Sprinkle lubricant on both sides of the saw.

- Hold the saw in the dominant hand and guide the back of the saw with the other hand for a few strokes until the saw is set in the kerf.
- Insert wedges as soon as possible, driving them snug. Take care not to hit the saw.
- Lubricate the blade as needed just before the push stroke. On a smaller log, the sawyer may be able to lubricate the far side of the saw just before the pull stroke. Be sure to lubricate both sides of the saw blade equally.
- As the cut is ending, use only the teeth at the end of the saw blade. This technique prevents the log from damaging the production cutters near the center of the saw when the log rolls or pinches the saw.

Single Bucking with Top Bind: Underbucking Required—

Underbucking is used when the log has a top bind and you can get under the log. The first cut must be started from the top because the top of the log is under compression. If the compression is not corrected, the kerf may close and pinch the saw.

After you have inserted the wedges and driven them snug, continue cutting down from the top, leaving enough uncut wood to support the log's weight. Because the top of the log is under compression, the bottom is under tension. The more compression you relieve, the greater the tension on the bottom of the log. The log will start to equalize this pressure by exerting pressure on the wedges. If you use two or more wedges spaced at the 10 and 2 o'clock positions, you can spread the force over a large area. If only one wedge is used at the 12 o'clock position, all the energy is directed to that relatively small area.

Remove the saw from the top cut and prepare to finish the cut from the bottom by underbucking. A log or rock can be placed under one side of the cut to support the log. That way, the log will be less likely to carry the saw to the ground when the cut is completed.

During sizeup, you determined which side of the severed log will probably remain the most stationary, providing the anchor point for the underbuck. A common mistake is to place the underbuck on the side that is easiest to reach. If this side of the log moves when the log is severed, the saw could be damaged.

To underbuck, use a mechanical underbuck or plant an ax in the log so the handle can be used as a support for the back of the saw (figure 5-23). Line up the underbuck grooves in the ax handle with the top saw kerf and swing the ax into the log forcefully.

Figure 5-23—An ax planted in the lower part of the log can work as an underbuck.

Oil in the underbuck groove will help the saw run easily and will reduce wear on the ax handle. Adjust the handle angle to allow room for the saw to be inserted and for the underbuck to be parallel to the saw kerf.

If you are placing an offset cut, allow for about ½ inch of offset toward the ax head.

If you are underbucking a compound cut, try to have the cuts match exactly because an offset could prevent the log from being freed. Several more wedges may have to be placed in the top cut to provide additional bearing pressure on the kerf faces, holding the log in place.

Lubricate both sides of the saw and the ax handle grooves.

Your body position will determine how to position the ax handle.

Place the back of the inverted saw in the underbuck groove. The saw typically starts out at an angle of about 45 degrees from horizontal. Your guiding hand holds the back of the saw. With a light downward pressure on the underbuck, push the saw forward. Pressure on the underbuck needs to be consistent on the push and pull strokes.

After several strokes, you can remove your hand and continue normal cutting. With continued downward pressure, the end of the saw will be doing more of the cutting and the saw blade will level out. As the cut nears completion, be prepared for the severed log to drop.

Single Bucking with Top Bind: Top Cutting—Several methods can be used to buck a log when there is top bind and not enough room to get the saw under the log for underbucking.

All sawing will be from the top. Do a good job of wedging to keep the kerf open. Follow the instructions for wedging (chapter 3). Periodically, drive all the wedges until they are snug. Do not allow wedges to contact the saw.

The cut will want to open up at the bottom. A log or other material can be placed under the log segment that will drop when the cut has been completed, reducing the distance it will fall.

Single Bucking with Bottom Bind: Top Cutting—When there is bottom bind and too little room to get the saw under the log for an undercut, all the cutting will be done from the top. The main problem with bottom binds is that standard wedging does not help. In addition, when the log is severed, segments of the log may drop or roll.

Cut the log as explained for top cutting with single bucking. Lightly place a small plastic wedge at the top of the cut. Do not drive the wedge in.

This wedge will show when the kerf begins to open. When the kerf opens, drive two fan-shaped metal wedges across the kerf. The point is to slow the opening of the kerf and the settling of the log.

As the kerf opens at the top, it exerts more and more compression on the uncut wood. If the force becomes too great, the uncut wood may slab off, possibly damaging the saw. The saw could be damaged even if the log does not slab.

When the log is sawed through, the log's weight may pull out the metal wedges, causing the log to drop and roll.

The sawyer needs to keep sawing or even speed up sawing to keep opening the kerf and relieving the compression pressure. The combination of using wedges to slow the kerf's opening and speeding up the cutting can prevent additional binding.

The best technique to reduce the effects of a bottom bind is to insert a stick into the opening saw kerf. A straight, finger-sized limb about a foot long can be inserted into the opening kerf at the top of the log (do not use plastic wedges).

As the kerf continues to open, the stick slides into the kerf. The stick does not drop to the back of the saw because it is too thick. As the cut is completed, the two halves of the severed log hinge on the stick. The bottom opens up, allowing the saw to drop free.

Single Bucking with Bottom Bind: Underbucking—If you have bottom bind and can get under the log, make the first cut from the bottom. In this case, wedging is not as critical. When the first cut is from the top, fan-shaped metal wedges can reduce the speed at which the kerf

opens. A stick can be inserted into the opening top cut if the log is large enough for the stick to fit into the kerf.

Single Bucking with End Bind—If more than one cut is being made, make the top cut first or make the cut where the log has the least amount of weight above the cut. This reduces the end bind on the second cut.

If you are cutting down directly from the top, use more plastic wedges around the cut, especially as it progresses below the centerline of the log. This reduces the possibility of binding.

Single Bucking with Side Bind—This is one of the most difficult and hazardous situations involving binds.

If there is room below the log for the saw's end to clear, cut the side with compression wood first. The finish cut is on the side with tension wood. Alternately saw and chop out wood with an ax. The saw should be in a nearly vertical position. Always find a safe position to make the finish cut.

If the log is on the ground in a side-bind situation, options are limited. For trees larger than 20 inches d.b.h., the only options are to place a cut beyond the side-bind area or to cut out the area with an ax.

Double-Bucking Techniques

New sawyers should master the skills of single bucking before learning double bucking.

The reasons to double buck are:

- Large logs can be sawed more easily by two sawyers.
- Two sawyers can transport equipment more easily than one.

Usually the uphill sawyer (the primary sawyer who will finish the cut) lubricates the saw and positions a guiding hand on the back of the saw for the first few strokes.

If you are going to roll the severed log out of the way, be sure to make a compound cut. The goal is for the sections of log to have as little surface resistance against each other as possible. The larger the log, the more careful the planning needed for the compound cut. Make the cuts where you will be safe and you will be able to move the log.

Your dominant hand (power hand) should be placed firmly around the saw's handle. Your other hand can rest on top of the handle to guide the saw and to help maintain your balance. Your dominant hand pulls the saw straight back to the side of your body. Sawyers often grip the saw too tightly with their guiding hand. This tends to pull the saw across their body.

ALWAYS pull—NEVER push!
Allow your partner to pull. Pushing may cause the saw to buckle.

As one sawyer pulls, the other sawyer keeps a relaxed grip on the handle. The sawyer neither pushes nor holds back. Holding back is called riding the saw, which makes it harder for the other sawyer to pull.

If you momentarily relax your grip, the saw will reposition itself in your hand for the pull stroke. Relaxing your grip also increases circulation in your hands and reduces fatigue.

If one sawyer needs to change body position (to drop to a kneeling position, for instance), the other sawyer needs to adjust the angle of the saw to accommodate the change.

Wedges should be placed as soon as there is room behind the back of the saw to insert them. For long logs, two wedges usually are inserted at the 10 and 2 o'clock positions and driven firmly until they are snug. If the wedges are not snug, the saw could be damaged.

Be sure the saw travels into and out of the kerf in a straight line. Look down the saw toward the other sawyer.

If the cut is going to be finished by single bucking, whenever *EITHER* sawyer determines it is time to stop sawing, both sawyers *STOP*. Do not allow your judgment to be swayed by your partner even if it means more single bucking will need to be done. Leave the downhill side as soon as possible.

If the log is going to be severed by double bucking (on flat terrain) be sure that the circle (the arc) of the saw remains parallel to the ground. Do not have one end higher than the other.

Usually the bottom bark has not been removed. Carefully look at the shavings. When they change to the color of the bark, the log has been severed and only the bark is holding it. If the log fell on mineral soil, the impact may have forced rocks into the bark. The rocks can dull the saw's teeth. Usually the cut is stopped when wood-colored fibers are no longer being removed.

When the cut is finished, or when it is being finished by single bucking, remove the handle on the downhill side of the saw and allow the uphill sawyer to pull the saw free. Make sure the downhill sawyer is in a safe location before the uphill sawyer continues the cut.

DO NOT remove the wedges before removing the saw. The wedges may be holding the log in position. When wedges are removed in these situations, the severed log shifts, binding the saw. If the wedges are loose enough to be lifted straight up, it is safe to do so—do not wiggle them out. Once the saw is free, the wedges can be safely removed while you are standing on the uphill side of the log. Be prepared for the log to move.

Felling Preparation and Techniques

Safety Considerations

Safety considerations for felling apply whether you are using chain saws or crosscut saws. The tree and the forces acting on it cannot tell the difference between handtools and power tools.

Situational Awareness

Analyze the felling job by considering:
- Species (live or dead)
- Size and length
- Soundness or defects
- Twin tops
- Widow makers and hangups
- Frozen wood
- Rusty (discolored) knots
- Punky (swollen and sunken) knots
- Spike top
- Footing
- Heavy snow loading
- Bark soundness
- Direction of lean
- Degree of lean (slight or great)
- Head lean or side lean
- Nests or insect holes
- Splits and frost cracks
- Deformities, such as those caused by mistletoe
- Heavy branches or uneven weight distribution
- Damage by lightning or fire

Check the base of the tree for:
- Thud (hollow) sound when struck
- Conks and mushrooms
- Rot and cankers
- Shelf or bracket fungi
- Wounds or scars
- Split trunk
- Insect activity

- Feeding holes
- Bark soundness
- Resin flow on bark
- Unstable root system or root protrusions

Examine surrounding terrain for:
- Steepness
- Irregularities in the ground
- Draws and ridges
- Rocks
- Stumps
- Loose logs
- Ground debris that can fly or kick up at the sawyer

Examine the immediate work area for:
- People, roads, or vehicles
- Powerlines
- Hangups and widow makers
- Snags
- Fire-weakened trees
- Reserve trees
- Structures
- Openings to fall trees into
- Other trees that may be affected
- Hazards such as trees, rocks, brush, or low-hanging limbs
- Other trees that may have to be felled first

Walk out and thoroughly check the intended lay where the tree is supposed to fall. Look for dead treetops, snags, and widow makers that may cause kickbacks, allow the tree to roll, or cause another tree or limb to become a hazard.

Escape routes must be predetermined paths where the sawyer can escape once the tree is committed to fall or has been bucked. Safety zones should be no less than 20 feet from the stump, preferably behind another tree that is sound and large enough to provide protection. Escape routes and safety zones should be 90 to 135 degrees from the direction of fall. Sawyers must select and prepare the work area and clear escape routes before starting the first cut.

Felling Sizeup

Most accidents are caused by falling debris. Watch overhead throughout the cut, glancing regularly at the saw, the kerf, and the top of the tree.

When you approach the tree to be felled, observe the top. Check for all overhead hazards that may come down during felling.

Look at the limbs. Are they heavy enough on one side to affect the desired felling direction? Do the limbs have heavy accumulations of ice and snow?

When the limbs entangle with the limbs of other trees, they can snap off or prevent the tree from falling after it has been cut.

Windspeeds higher than 15 miles per hour may be strong enough to affect the tree's fall. When there are strong winds, stop felling. Other trees and snags in the area also may blow over. Erratic winds require special safety considerations.

Check all snags in the immediate area for soundness. A snag may fall at any time with a gust of wind, the vibration of a tree fall, or as the snag's roots succumb to rot. If it is safe to do so, begin by felling any snag in the cutting area that is a hazard.

Clear small trees, brush, and debris from the base of the tree. Remove all material that could cause you to trip or lose balance. Also remove material that will interfere with your use of the saw, wedges, and ax. Be careful not to fatigue yourself with unnecessary swamping. Remove only as much material as necessary to allow you to work safely around the base of the tree and to provide escape routes.

The importance of sound holding (hinge) wood cannot be overemphasized. Determine the condition of the holding wood by sounding it with an ax. Look up while doing so, in case any debris is dislodged. Check for frost cracks or other weak areas in the holding wood. The desired felling direction can be adjusted to compensate for weak areas in the holding wood. The depth of the undercut also can be adjusted to take advantage of the holding area.

Most trees have two natural leans: the predominant head lean and the secondary side lean. Both must be considered when determining the desired felling direction. The desired felling direction usually can be chosen within 45 degrees of the combined lean, provided there is enough sound holding (hinge) wood to work with, especially in the corners of the undercut.

Use a plumb bob or ax to evaluate the tree's lean. Project a vertical line up from the center of the tree's butt and determine if the tree's top lies to the right or left of the projected line.

A pistol-grip tree has a curve at the base of the trunk and may appear to be leaning in one direction while most of the weight of the tree is actually leaning in another direction.

Look at the treetop from at least two different spots at right angles to each other. You will do so again during the sizeup, but take every opportunity to determine the correct lean.

In summary, during felling sizeup:

- Observe the top.
- Check for snags.
- Swamp out the base.
- Assess the soundness of the holding wood.
- Assess the lean.

Establishing Escape Routes and Safety Zones

With the desired felling direction in mind, determine your escape routes. Consider the side of the tree where you will make your final cut and select a path that will take you at least 20 feet behind the stump when the tree begins to fall. Don't choose a path directly behind the tree. It is best to prepare two escape routes in case you switch your location on the final cut (figure 5-24).

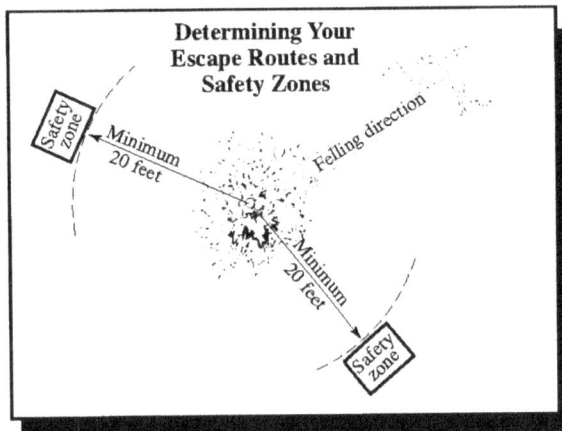

Determining Your Escape Routes and Safety Zones

Figure 5-24—Keep the felling direction in mind when planning escape routes.

Look for a large solid tree or rock for protection. Safety zones must be at least 20 feet away from the stump and not directly behind it. Practice the escape routes, making sure that debris that could trip you is cleared.

Walk out the intended lay of the tree (figure 5-25) and look for any obstacles that could cause the tree to kick back over the stump or cause the butt to jump or pivot as the tree hits the ground. Look for any small trees or snags that could be thrown into your escape routes. Ensure that the cutting area is clear of people.

Reexamine the escape routes. Be sure that your chosen routes will be the safest escapes—*before* you begin to cut.

Figure 5-25—Check the intended lay of the tree for obstacles.

Placing the Undercut

After the escape routes are established, specific methods shall be used to cut the tree. We are going to discuss just the conventional undercut because of its broad application for all timber types and because it provides a solid foundation from which to learn additional cutting techniques.

Before beginning the undercut, prepare the tree for cutting (figure 5-26). Bark should be removed to:

- Keep the saw sharp.
- Make wedges more effective.
- See how the cuts are lining up.

It takes three cuts to fell a tree. Two cuts form the undercut (or face cut) and the third forms the back cut. The correct relationship of these cuts results in safe and effective tree felling. Before discussing the felling procedure, we will analyze the mechanics of the felling cuts. Undercutting and back cutting construct the hinge that controls the fall of the tree and the direction of fall.

The undercut serves two purposes. First, it allows the tree to fall in a given direction by removing the tree's support in the direction of the face. Second, it enables control because the tree slips off—rather than jumps off—the stump.

Figure 5-26—An ax can be used to remove the bark.

Ways to make the undercut:
- Make the undercut with a crosscut saw, or
- Make the horizontal cut with a crosscut saw and chop the undercut out with an ax, or
- Chop out the entire undercut with an ax.

Chopping Out the Undercut With an Ax—Although this approach may appear to be the hardest, it has advantages in certain situations. If this method is used, the cut should be level so the back cut, which is parallel to the undercut, will be level also.

Advantages of chopping out the undercut:
- Chopping out the undercut is about as fast as sawing the undercut for smaller trees.
- Chopping out the undercut may be best in restricted areas where one side of the tree does not offer standing room for the sawyer or does not have adequate clearance for the end of the saw.
- Chopping out the undercut will allow the sawyer to limit the number of cuts. It is hard to apply saw oil to

the bottom edge of a saw in the horizontal felling position. Chopping out the undercut is especially useful if the tree is extremely pitchy.
- Chopping out the undercut is a good alternative when the saw handles cannot be vertical, or when a stiff bucking saw is used, or for any combination of factors that lead to an uncomfortable sawing position.

Using a Crosscut Saw and an Ax—Make the horizontal cut with a saw and chop out the undercut with an ax. The horizontal saw cut is put in first, allowing the sawyer to place a level cut more easily. The ax helps keep the cut free of any dutchmans.

Making the Undercut With a Crosscut Saw—When making the undercut, take care not to bypass the cuts. When the cuts don't meet exactly, they create a dutchman (figure 5-27).

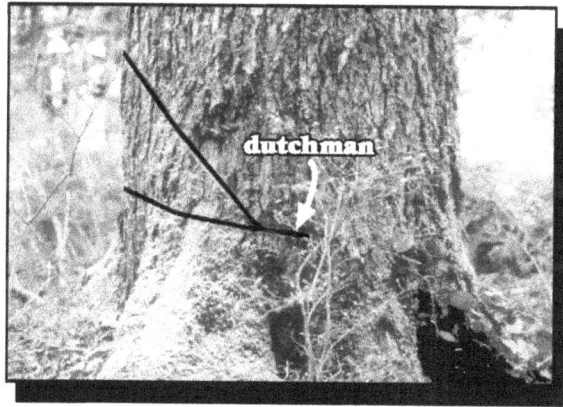

Figure 5-27—When the sloping cut and the horizontal cut do not meet exactly, a dutchman is formed. This kerf-wide cut makes the direction of the tree's fall harder to predict. It can also cause the tree to barber chair, lifting the log off the stump and placing the sawyers at great risk.

ALWAYS pull—NEVER push!
Allow your partner to pull. Pushing may cause the saw to buckle.

Observe overhead hazards and look up often during the undercut (figure 5-28).

Figure 5-28—Hazard trees need to be removed to prevent anyone from working under them.

Ideally, the undercut is made in the same direction as the tree's lean. Depending on structures, roads, other trees, and trails, the desired felling direction may be to one side or the other of the lean. Normally, the desired direction should be less than 45 degrees from the lean.

If there is any danger from above, such as snags, the sawyer should cut while standing to make it easier to watch the top and escape more quickly. The horizontal cut is a level cut. The horizontal cut dictates the direction of fall if the relationships of the three cuts are maintained. After selecting the desired felling direction, estimate one-third the tree's diameter and begin the horizontal cut.

The specific direction of the undercut is determined by gunning the saw (figure 5-29). Place the back of the saw against the back of the undercut. The saw's teeth should point in the direction the tree should fall.

Figure 5-29—Gunning the saw helps determine the specific direction of the undercut. (Photo has been digitally altered to remove distracting items.)

Trees with leans may not allow you to insert the horizontal cut as deep as one-third of the tree's diameter without pinching the saw.

The sloping cut needs to be angled so that when the undercut closes the tree is fully committed to your planned direction of fall. As the cut closes, the holding wood breaks.

A general rule for the sloping cut is that is should be at a 45-degree angle. Remember that it is important that the undercut not close until the tree is fully committed to your planned direction of fall (figure 5-30). Line up the sloping cut with the horizontal cut so that they meet, but do not cross. When the cuts cross, a dutchman is formed. If the tree were felled with a dutchman, first the dutchman would close, then the tree would split vertically (barber chair), or the holding wood would break off. Felling control would be lost. Practicing on high stumps will help you become skilled at lining up these cuts.

CUTS TO FELL A TREE

Back cut · Sloping cut · Undercut · Horizontal cut

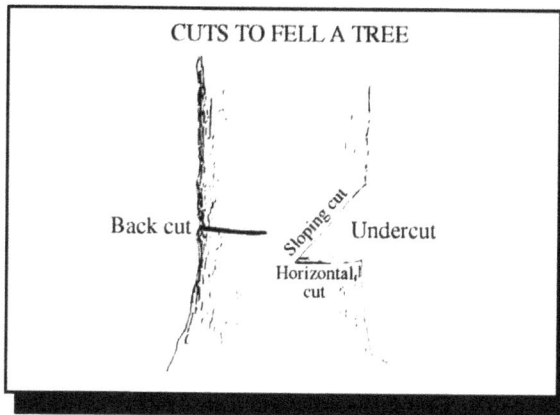

Figure 5-30—An undercut and a back cut are required to fell a tree. A horizontal cut and a sloping cut make up the undercut. Often, the sloping cut is made with an ax instead of a crosscut saw. The back cut is the third cut needed to fell a tree.

The holding wood is the wood immediately behind the undercut. The most important portion of the holding wood is in the very corners of the cut (the first 4 to 8 inches inside the tree). The horizontal and sloping cut must not overlap in this region. If they do, the undercut must be cleaned up so no dutchman is left in these corners. Care must be taken not to cut the undercut too deeply while cleaning up. This will affect the amount of room available for wedges.

Once the undercut has been cleaned, place the saw back in the face and recheck the gunning direction. The saw handle will point in the felling direction. If the tree is not gunned in the direction that you want it to fall, extend the horizontal and sloping cuts as needed.

Cutting the Back Cut

The third cut needed to fall a tree is the back cut. The relationship of this cut to the undercut is important for proper tree positioning and the sawyers' safety.

The best way to envision these cuts is by the use of a rectangle (figure 5-31). The bottom corner is the back of the horizontal cut. The opposite upper corner will be the back of the back cut.

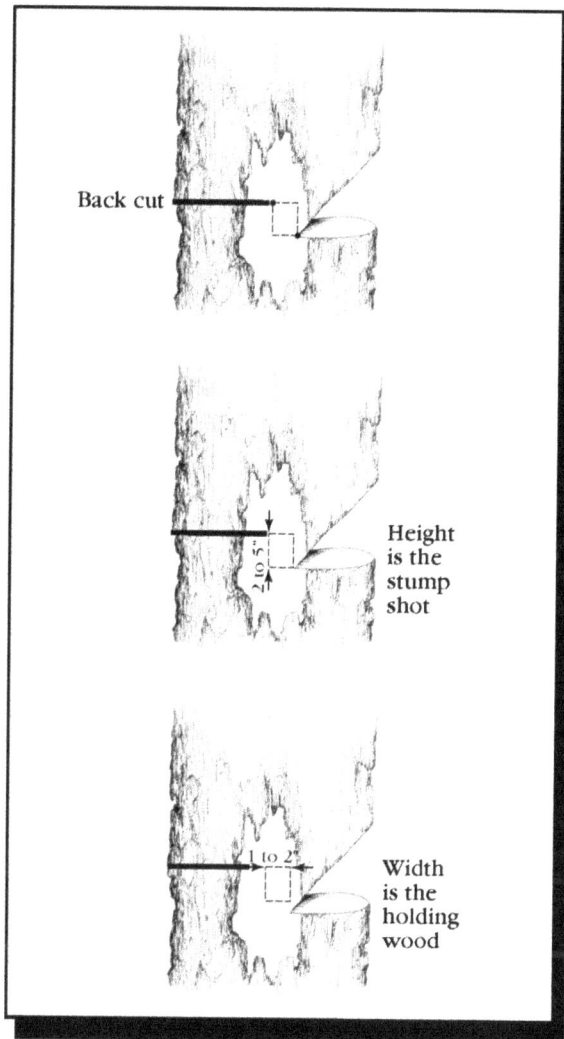

Back cut · Height is the stump shot · Width is the holding wood

Figure 5-31—An imaginary rectangle can help the sawyer understand the importance of the back cut. The dimensions of this rectangle are based on a 24-inch-diameter tree.

The height of the rectangle is referred to as the stump shot. It is an antikickback device to prevent the tree from kicking back over the stump if it hits another tree as it falls. Preventing kickback is especially important to sawyers who are felling trees through standing timber.

The width of the rectangle is the holding wood. As the back cut is made, sawyers must be sure not to cut this wood. Maintaining the holding wood is the key to safe and effective felling.

85

Hold the saw level so that the back cut will be level when the cut is complete. You want to be sure that when the cut is finished, it will line up with the top corner of the opposite rectangle. If the cut is angled, wedging effectiveness and the height of the stump shot could be altered.

Remove thick bark immediately above and below the back cut's kerf where wedges will be placed. The bark could compress, reducing the lifting power of the wedges.

Keep at least four wedges and an ax readily accessible while making the back cut. The size of the wedges depends on the tree's diameter.

If the tree begins to move and the saw is stuck, do not hesitate— LEAVE THE SAW!

If two sawyers are working together, before cutting, identify who will take the saw to the escape route.

When the sawyer with the saw is watching from a safe location, the other sawyer can drive the wedges, causing the tree to lift and commit to fall. When the tree begins to move, the sawyer can escape along the escape route from the stump.

While in a safe location, both sawyers need to continue looking up for overhead hazards. There is a tendency to look at the tree as it hits the ground, leaving the sawyers unaware of limbs that may be thrown back from other trees near the stump. LOOK UP. If rocks or other material are dislodged when the tree hits the ground, yell a warning.

For crosscut saw felling operations, if two sawyers are needed or if an observer/spotter is needed, justification for additional personnel, and the implementation process, shall be documented in the JHA, as required by the Health and Safety Code Handbook.

Chapter 6—Field Proficiency

The instructor will work with the students using the techniques taught in the classroom. Students will perform limbing, bucking, and felling under the guidance of a qualified instructor and will be evaluated on their skill level.

Instructor's Responsibilities

The instructor must take an active role in training and certifying the students. *The instructor needs to demonstrate the proper skills and work with the students to ensure that they gain the skills needed to operate chain saws and crosscut saws safely.*

The instructor needs to make honest, constructive assessments when evaluating students. The instructor is responsible for certifying that the students demonstrate the operational skills to do the work safely. If they don't, the instructor should document the additional training needed on their sawyer evaluation forms.

The instructor can restrict the students' operational activities (limbing, brushing, slashing, bucking, felling) to specific sizes and types of trees in specific locations or regions.

Students must understand that further training may be required before sawing in different regions because of the differences in tree species, wood properties, and tree sizes.

During the field training sessions, safety should be the number one concern of instructors and students. Instructors must do a thorough job of planning before beginning the field training sessions.

- Do not mix bucking and felling sessions.
- When selecting a cutting area, determine the needs of the students. Work with district or forest staff to locate a site that is suitable, has good access, and does not have safety hazards that cannot be mitigated. Obtain all proper clearances through the environmental analysis process.
- Recommended class size is 12 students per instructor.
- Prepare a job hazard analysis in advance that includes first-aid procedures and emergency evacuation plans. Use the *Health and Safety Code Handbook* and safety information in this chapter to help develop these plans.
- Conduct a tailgate session that includes all safety aspects of the field proficiency exercises, first-aid procedures and emergency evacuation plans.
- Ensure that all students have all safety items listed on the sawyer evaluation form (figure 6-1).

Sawyer Evaluation Form

Name_____ Date_____ Phone_____

Address_____

District/agency_____ Forest_____

Previously certified?_____ Chain saw?_____ Level_____ Where_____ Year_____

SAFETY EQUIPMENT
____Hardhat
____Long-sleeved shirt (optional for crosscut saw)
____Gloves
____Boots
____Wedges
____Eye protection
____Ax
____Chaps (optional for crosscut saw)
____Hearing protection (chain saw only)
____Saw sheath

HAZARD ANALYSIS
____Top
____Widow maker
____Bark
____Leaners
____Hangups
____Determine soundness and lean(s)
____Snags/green-tree hazards
____Root wads/loose logs
____Other

SAW USE
____Saw and ax condition
____Safe, comfortable body position
____Throttle lock use (chain saw only)
____Thumb placement (chain saw only)
____Starting procedure
____Bar tip use, general (chain saw only)
____Boring, specific (chain saw only)
____Handle placement (crosscut saw only)
____Ax/saw selection
____Cut preparation, bark removal (crosscut saw only)
____Saw passing (crosscut saw only)

FELLING PROCEDURE
____Escape routes/safety zones
____Swampout
____Plumbing lean
____Thumb placement (chain saw only)
____Undercutting
____Wedging procedure
____Warning shout
____Back cutting
____Cutting with head up
____Handle removal (crosscut saw only)
____Gunning cut
____Use of gunning sights

____Use of escape route/safety zone
____Leave it

STUMP ANALYSIS
____Felled to desired lay
____Felled to other lay
____Undercut positioning
____Back cut
____Horizontal cut
____Sloping cut
____Undercut as a whole
____Holding wood
____Stump shot, height
____Stump shot, holding wood
____Dutchman, one corner
____Dutchman, both corners

FELLLING AREA
____Crew safety
____Secure area
____Communication
____Cleanup

LIMBING
____Overhead dangers
____Body positioning
____Thumb placement (chain saw only)
____Spring poles/tension/compression
____Limb removal sequence
____Use of bar tip (chain saw only)
____Use of ax

BUCKING
____Overhead analysis
____Ground/hazard analysis
____Bind/tension/compression analysis
____Thumb placement (chain saw only)
____Use of pie-shaped cuts (chain saw only)
____Wedge techniques
____Cutting sequence
____Kerf observation
____Release cut movement
____Protection of saw (crosscut saw only)
____Double bucking (crosscut saw only)
____Compound cut
____Underbucking (crosscut saw only)
____Single bucking (crosscut saw only)
____Offset cutting (crosscut saw only)

Figure 6-1—Sawyer evaluation form.

Sawyer Evaluation Form

COMMENTS

Use this space to make additional comments about such things as attitude, technical skills, verbal skills (weak, strong, and so forth).

_____

_____

_____

_____

_____

_____

SKILL LEVEL

Chain saw rating_____ (A = Apprentice, B = Intermediate, C = Advanced)

Crosscut saw rating_____ (A = Apprentice, B = Intermediate, C = Advanced)

Instructor/certifier for: Chain saw_____ Crosscut saw_____ Level_____

RESTRICTIONS (if any)_____

_____

Classroom instruction given at_____ Date_____

Instructor's signature_____ Title_____ Level_____

Recommended by (if applicable)_____ Title_____

Field examination given at_____ Date_____

Examiner's signature_____ Title_____ Level_____

Supervisor's signature_____ Title_____ Level_____

Figure 6-1—(continued).

Personal Protective Equipment

- Hardhat.
- Eye protection.
- Hearing protection (for chain saw use only).
- Gloves (cut resistant for chain filing).
- Long-sleeved shirt (optional for crosscut saw use).
- Chain saw chaps (recommended to overlap boots by at least 2 inches, optional for crosscut saw use). Only saw chaps provided by the General Services Administration meeting the most current Forest Service specifications (6170–4) are approved for purchase and use.
- Heavy-duty, 8-inch-high, laced cut-resistant or leather boots with nonskid soles and adequate ankle support.

General Equipment

- Type IV first-aid kit.
- Fire extinguisher (for chain saw use only).
- Proper saw for the job (for chain saws, a full-wrap handlebar is recommended for felling).
- Fully operational chain brake.
- Chain (filed and maintained).
- Chain saw wrench.
- Approved safety container for fuel.
- Chain and bar oil container (clearly marked).
- Proper wedges for the work project (wooden wedges not permitted).
- Single-bit ax or maul (3 to 5 pounds).
- Bumper spikes (for chain saw use only).

The instructor must be aware of the activities taking place in all cutting areas and ensure that students follow correct safety procedures at all times.

Many safety issues are specific to tree felling. These issues must be discussed by the instructor and the student before each tree is cut. In addition, the instructor must discuss the safety procedures to follow in case of an accident.

90

A fully qualified instructor must be at the base of the tree within a few feet of the sawyer to monitor the process and prevent accidents. Justification for having a second person at the base of the tree must be documented in the JHA.

Conducting Field Training for Sawyers

Secure Felling Area

Many safety issues can be addressed by establishing a secure felling area, which must be identified and managed. The area needs to be at least two-and-one-half times the height of the tree being felled, in all directions. On hillsides with steep slopes, the entire downhill side will be included in the secure area.

No one shall be allowed in the secured felling area without authorization by the sawyer and instructor.

A safety zone will be established outside the secure area. Everyone must remain there until all felling is completed and the sawyer has shouted *All clear.*

Whenever practical, the safety zone should be opposite the direction of the planned fall, and at least two-and-one-half times the height of the tree being felled.

One person shall be responsible for maintaining reliable communications with the sawyer and with people in the safety zone to ensure that no one enters the secured felling area.

A road or trail guard will be set up on all roads and trails entering and leaving the secured felling area to prevent members of the public or other employees from entering the area. Effective communications must exist between the guards and the sawyer.

Before leaving the secured felling area, the sawyer needs to ensure that no hazards remain (such as hangups, unstable logs, or other dangers).

To protect the lives of employees, contractors, and the public, the sawyer must adhere to these standards. Supervisors and all employees must understand and follow these standards.

Monitoring Cutting Procedures

The instructor needs to monitor cutting procedures and take corrective actions or discontinue cutting if problems develop. Common problems include:

- Inaccurate gunning (sighting) that may cause the tree to fall in the wrong direction or get hung up in another tree.
- Too deep an undercut that may cause a tree to go over backward or fall before the undercut is complete.
- A potential barber chair. Recognize this situation before it occurs.
- Accidental or intentional removal of all or part of the holding wood.
- Any changes in the wind or the tree's lean. Is the student aware of these changes?
- Wedging too late or other improper wedging.

Skill Demonstrations

Brushing and Bucking—Students shall:
- Demonstrate the proper starting method (for chain saws only).
- Demonstrate the ability to analyze special hazards associated with limbing, brushing, and bucking.
- Demonstrate the ability to brush out an area safely, limb a tree or log, and buck a log.

Tree Felling—Students shall:
- Demonstrate the ability to determine and prepare a safe felling area.
- Demonstrate the ability to identify correctly any special hazards associated with tree felling.
- Demonstrate the ability to fell safely a tree to a predetermined lay.
- Demonstrate the ability to do a stump analysis of the student's evaluation tree.

When students have successfully completed training, the instructor will award a chain saw or crosscut training certificate. Students also will receive the appropriate pocket-size certification card. Instructors shall include any restrictions or endorsements on the sawyer evaluation form and the certification card.

Glossary

This glossary is adapted from the S-212 *Wildland Fire Chain Saws* training program.

Ax—A part of the faller's safety equipment used for pounding and chopping. It also can be used to plumb the lean of a tree.

Back Cut—The last of the three cuts required to fell a tree. Locate the back cut on the opposite side of the tree from the undercut (face) and at least 2 inches (the stump shot) above the horizontal cut of the undercut (face). The back cut must never be continued to a point at which no holding wood remains.

Barber Chair—A tree that splits vertically when it is being felled. Generally, this is a result of improper facing or back cutting. A portion of the fallen tree is left on the stump.

Bind—A series of pressures in a felled tree resulting from objects (such as terrain or stumps) that prevent the tree from lying flat on the ground. The two major components of bind are compression and tension. Binds determine the technique and procedure used while bucking.

Blowdown—An area of timber blown over by strong winds or storms.

Bole—A tree stem thick enough for saw timber or large poles.

Boring—Using the nose or tip of the guide bar to saw into the tree while felling or bucking.

Bottom Bind—One of the four basic tree positions commonly encountered while bucking. A tree with a bottom bind is tensioned on top and compressed on the bottom.

Brushing—Removing the brush and shrubs while swamping out a work area.

Buck—Sawing through the bole of a tree after it has been felled.

Butt—The base of a tree stem.

Calks—Heavy boots containing numerous steel spikes (calks).

Conventional Undercut—The sloping cut taken from the butt of the tree.

Corners—The holding wood on either outside edge of the tree.

CPR—Cardiopulmonary resuscitation.

Danger Tree—A standing tree that presents a hazard because of conditions such as deterioration or physical damage to the root system, trunk, stem, or limbs, and the direction and lean of the tree.

Dogs (Bumper Spikes)—A chain saw accessory designed for felling and bucking. Chain saw dogs increase the sawyer's efficiency during felling and bucking operations.

Dolmar—Container for holding saw fuel and oil.

DOT—U.S. Department of Transportation.

Double Jack—A long-handled sledge hammer used to drive splitting and lifting wedges.

Dutchman—A portion of the undercut that is not removed. A dutchman generally results when the horizontal and sloping cuts of the undercut do not meet or extend beyond each other. A dutchman is very hazardous because it can change the felling direction.

End Bind—One of the four basic tree positions commonly encountered while bucking. An end bind occurs on steep terrain where the force of gravity closes the bucking cuts.

EPA—U.S. Environmental Protection Agency.

Escape Route—A predetermined path used by fallers when felling or bucking. Determine the direction and distance of the escape route and clear the route before cutting.

Face Cut—See undercut.

First-Aid Kit—A kit including bloodborne pathogen protective equipment (as a minimum, disposable gloves, face masks, eye protection, and CPR clear-mouth barriers) in addition to standard first-aid supplies.

Forest Service Approved—An item that meets Forest Service specifications or conforms to Forest Service drawings.

Guide Bar—The part of the chain saw that the chain travels on. Improper use of the bar (particularly the top and bottom of the bar at the end of the bar's nose) results in kickbacks and saw injuries.

Gunning (Sighting)—Aligning the gunning mark with the desired felling direction. Because the gunning mark is at a 90-degree angle to the bar, the exact position of the undercut can be established easily in relation to the desired felling direction.

Hanging Wedge—A fan-shaped metal wedge.

Hangup—A situation in which a tree is lodged in another tree and does not fall to the ground.

Head Lean—One of the two natural leaning forces found in most trees. Head lean is more pronounced than side lean.

Holding Wood—Section of wood located between the undercut and the back cut. Its purpose is to prevent the tree from permanently slipping from the stump before it has been committed to the undercut. It also helps direct where the tree will fall. The holding wood must never be completely sawed through.

Hinge Wood—Same as holding wood.

Horizontal Undercut—The first of the two cuts required for the undercut. This level cut is at least one-third the diameter of the tree.

Itinerary—Planned route of travel, date of travel, destination, and estimated times of departure and arrival.

Jackstraw—Area where trees have been blown or fallen down in crisscross fashion.

JHA—Job hazard analysis.

Kerf—The slot a saw's cutters make in the wood.

Kickback—A strong thrust of the saw back toward the faller, generally resulting from improper use of the guide bar's nose or from pinching the bar in a cut.

Lay—Refers either to the position in which a felled tree is lying or the intended location of a standing tree after it has been felled.

Lead—The established direction in which all trees in a quarter or strip are to be felled, usually governed by the terrain of the area, its general slope, or the skid road system.

Lean—The tilt of a tree away from its vertical position. Often two leans (such as head lean and side lean) may affect the same tree.

Leaner—A tree that leans heavily.

Limbing—Removing the branches from a felled or standing tree.

MSDS—Material safety data sheet. A compilation of information required under the Occupational Safety and Health Administration's Hazard Communication Standard that outlines the identity of hazardous chemicals; health, physical, and fire hazards; exposure limits; and storage and handling precautions.

NIOSH—National Institute for Occupational Safety and Health.

Offside—The opposite side of the tree from where the faller stands while bucking or felling.

OSHA—U.S. Department of Labor Occupational Safety and Health Administration.

Pie-Shaped Cut—A section sawed from a log during bucking to allow for the directional pressures of various binds. Removing a pie-shaped section of a log minimizes splits and slabs.

PPE—Personal protective equipment and clothing, protective shields, and barriers.

Pistol-Grip Tree—A tree with a curve at the base of the trunk that makes it difficult to identify the tree's lean.

Sapwood—The outer layers of wood in growing trees that contain living cells and reserve material such as starch.

Side Bind—One of the four basic tree positions commonly encountered while bucking. A tree in a side bind is under compression on one side and under tension on the other.

Side Lean—One of the two natural leans found in many trees. Side lean is less pronounced than head lean.

Sitback—Refers to a tree that settles back on the stump, closing the back cut's kerf. Sitback usually occurs because of wind or because the tree's lean has not been determined properly.

Slabbing—A lateral split generally caused by improper technique or by an improper sequence of bucking cuts.

Sloping Cut—The second of the two cuts required to undercut a tree. This cut must be angled to allow a wide opening for the undercut.

Snag—Any standing dead tree.

Sound—Wood that is not rotten.

Spider—A gauge used for setting crosscut saw teeth.

Spike Top—A live tree that has a dead top.

Spring Pole—A limb or sapling that is bent under a tree or other weight.

Stump Shot—Two inches or more difference in the height of the horizontal cut of the undercut (face) and the back cut. The difference in height establishes a step that will prevent a tree from jumping back over the stump toward the faller.

Swamp Out—Clear out brush and other material around the base of trees and the areas where trees will be bucked to provide safe footing and to remove materials that could cause the saw to kick back.

Top Bind—One of the four basic tree positions commonly encountered while bucking. A tree with top bind is under compression on top and under tension on the bottom.

Undercut (Face Cut)—A section of wood sawed and removed from a tree's base. Its removal allows the tree to fall and helps direct where the tree will fall. The face is comprised of two separate cuts, one horizontal, the other sloping. The horizontal cut must be at least one-third the diameter of the tree. The sloping cut must have enough angle to allow a wide opening. The two cuts must not cross each other.

USDA—U.S. Department of Agriculture.

Wedge—A plastic or magnesium tool used by a faller to redistribute a tree's weight in the desired direction and to prevent a tree from falling backward. It also is used while bucking to prevent the guide bar from being pinched.

Widow Maker—A loose limb, top, or piece of bark that may fall on anyone working beneath it.

About the Authors

Jerry Taylor Wolf received a bachelor's degree in education from Indiana State University and a master's degree in journalism at the University of Montana. She began her Forest Service career as a civil engineering technician on the Flathead National Forest. She served as a survey party chief on the Beaverhead-Deerlodge and Lolo National Forests. In 1994, she came to the Missoula Technology and Development Center to work as a mechanical engineering technician. She is now a technical writer/editor. E-mail: *jtwolf@fs.fed.us*.

Chuck Whitlock was a project leader at MTDC from 1998 until his retirement in 2002. He specialized in safety and health and fire management safety projects. He served as a type I safety officer on national incident management teams and as a zone fire management officer on the Wallowa-Whitman National Forest. Chuck worked on the Plumas, Cleveland, and Fremont National Forests before coming to the center.

Library Card

Wolf, Jerry Taylor; Whitlock, Chuck. 2006. Chain saw and crosscut saw training course: student's guidebook. Tech. Rep. 0667-2805-MTDC. Missoula, MT: U.S. Department of Agriculture Forest Service, Missoula Technology and Development Center. 96 p.

Includes materials for students taking a 16- to 32-hour course for basic to intermediate chain saw and crosscut saw users. The course is designed to provide the technical knowledge and skills employees or volunteers need to use these tools safely. A companion instructor's guidebook (0667-2804-MTDC) and the student's guidebook both include sections on: course information and safety requirements, glossary, sample job hazard analysis, additional information for sawyers, chain saw use and maintenance, chain saw tasks and techniques, crosscut saw tasks and techniques, and a chapter explaining the field proficiency test. The instructor's guidebook also includes special notes for the instructor.

Keywords: class activities, instruction, safety, safety at work, teaching materials

Single copies of the *Chain Saw and Crosscut Saw Training Course* CD (0667–2C01–MTDC) may be ordered from:

USDA Forest Service, MTDC
5785 Hwy. 10 West
Missoula, MT 59808-9361
Phone: 406-329-3978
Fax: 406-329-3719
E-mail: *wo_mtdc_pubs@fs.fed.us*

Electronic copies of MTDC's documents are available on the Internet at: *http://www.fs.fed.us/t-d* (Username: t-d, Password: t-d).

For additional information, contact Gary Hoshide at MTDC.
Phone: 406-329-1029
Fax: 406-329-3719
E-mail: *ghoshide@fs.fed.us*

Forest Service and Bureau of Land Management employees can search a more complete collection of MTDC's documents, videos, and CDs on their internal computer networks at: *http://fsweb.mtdc.wo.fs.fed.us/search*.